C000142572

KS2
Success

Grammar, Punctuation and Spelling

Birds is flying in the garden. ✗
Birds are flying in the garden. ✓

Rachel Axten-Higgs

Contents

Grammar

Punctuation

Spelling

Nouns and pronouns

What is a noun?

A noun is a word that is used to name a person, place, animal or thing. Underline the nouns in these sentences.

1 The **children** jumped. 2 The **car** was huge. 3 **London** is big.

4 The **dog** was tiny. 5 The **lion** roared. 6 **Freya** giggled.

What is a pronoun?

A pronoun does the same job as a noun but can be used instead of a noun to prevent a piece of writing being too repetitive. Pronouns are words that refer to a noun, e.g. he, she, his, her, it, yours, they, their.

Write the correct pronouns in the spaces to ensure the sentences make sense.

1 Claire had to walk to work because _her_ car had broken down. _She_ was not very happy about _her_ situation.

2 Mark cycled to _his_ place of work because _he_ wanted to stay fit and healthy.

3 Hannah paddled to work in _her_ canoe as _she_ worked on a remote island in the middle of the sea.

Using the correct pronoun

It is easy to mix up some pronouns, for instance *they* and *them* or *me* and *my*. You need to take care when writing to make sure you do not do this!

Circle the correct word in each sentence.

1 Them / They are my favourite. 4 I like my / me friends.

2 Are you friends with them / they ? 5 Are you cross with my / me ?

3 When are them / they coming? 6 My / Me best friend is Rudolph!

Top Tip

When writing pronouns in replacement of nouns it is important to think about what the noun is. Read your sentences back to check that they make sense and refer to the noun properly.

Identifying pronouns

Underline the pronouns in these sentences.

1   The coach asked the team to work harder because <u>he</u> wanted them to do their best.

2   The boys stood at the top of the mountain and looked at the beautiful view. <u>They</u> were amazed; it was beautiful.

Write the pronoun:

3   Write the pronoun that refers to the boys from Q2 above.

    <u>? help?</u>

4   Write the pronoun that refers to the view from Q2 above.

    <u>? help?</u>

Different types of noun

There are four types of noun:

• **Proper** nouns refer to particular places or people, e.g. France / Claire. They start with a capital letter.

• **Common** nouns name a kind of person or thing, e.g. boy / day.

• **Collective** nouns refer to a group or collection of people or things, e.g. crowd / flock (of birds).

• **Abstract** nouns generally refer to things that exist but cannot be seen, heard, smelt, felt or tasted, e.g. sleep / hope.

In the sentences below, mark the proper nouns (PR), the common nouns (CM), the collective nouns (CL), and the abstract nouns (AB).

1   The apples _(CM)_ were dropped from the sky __?__ by a flock of birds _(CL)_.

2   London _(PR)_ is the capital city _(CM)_ of England _PR_. _(PR)_

3   The brave knight _____ had courage _____ to fight the dragon _____.

4   The team _____ were in high spirits after they won their trophy _____.

Verbs and adverbs

What is a verb?

A verb is a doing or being word. It is often an action. Every sentence must contain a verb – otherwise it is not a sentence.

Underline the verbs in these sentences.

1 The girl cried
2 The lorry stopped
3 I went to the shops
4 The ant was small
5 The lady smiled
6 Claire worked hard

Verb tenses

A verb can change the tense of a sentence to show when something happens, i.e. in the past, present or future. For example:

- I ran to the shops. (past tense)
- I am running to the shops. (present tense)
- I will run to the shops. (future tense)

Rewrite these sentences in the past tense.

1 I am walking to school.

_____

2 I will be eating chips.

_____

3 I will be learning how to speak French.

_____

4 Fill in the table to show how the verb 'to run' changes.

Subject	Present	Past	Future
I	I run	I ran	I will run
You			
He/she/it			She will run
We			
They	They run		

What is an adverb?

Adverbs are words that describe the verb (they give extra information to the reader about how the verb is happening).

For example, in the sentence *The children played loudly,* the word *loudly* is the adverb.

Underline the adverbs.

1   The cup fell gently.

2   The news spread quickly.

3   The children worked hard.

4   The dolphin performed happily.

Top Tip

Lots of adverbs end with the suffix –ly (although not all). It can be helpful to identify the verb in the sentence first in order to find the adverb.

Adverbs describing adjectives

Adverbs can also be used to describe adjectives.

In each sentence, underline the adjective and circle the adverb.

1   The flowers were extremely pretty.

2   The table was very heavy.

3   The dress was completely ruined.

4   The car was quite dirty.

Top Tip

It is really important to read the sentence carefully and check your answer.

Identifying verbs and adverbs

In each sentence, circle the verb and underline the adverb.

1   The kind boy ran quickly to the shops.

2   The colourful curtains hung neatly on the rail.

3   The silent animal crept cautiously through the bushes.

4   The noisy car roared loudly down the dusty road.

Adjectives

What are adjectives?

Adjectives are describing words and are used to describe the noun in a sentence.

Underline the adjective in these phrases.

1 The bright sun
2 The short girl
3 A beautiful baby
4 The colourful flower
5 The angry driver
6 The noisy, smelly car

Using adjectives in your writing

An adjective can make your writing more exciting for your reader as it gives more detail about the noun that you are describing, helping readers to create powerful pictures in their heads.

For example, *The cat sat on the mat* is not as interesting as *The contented cat sat on the warm, sheepskin mat.*

Rewrite these sentences using adjectives to make them more exciting.

Top Tip

Remember to use a range of adjectives in your writing so that it doesn't become dull. Be careful not to overuse words like 'nice' and 'big'.

1 The fish swam in the tank.

_____

2 The children played in the park.

_____

3 The lion roared at the keeper.

_____

Using exciting adjectives

In the box, write **eight** adjectives that you could use instead of 'nice'.

Comparative adjectives

Comparative adjectives are used to compare two nouns. For instance, *the girl is taller* than the boy. If an adjective has more than two syllables, then the word **more** is used.

Circle the comparative adjective in each sentence.

1   The beautiful cheetah ran faster than the frightened monkey.

2   The pretty flowers were more colourful than the prickly shrubs.

3   There were more chocolates than sweets in the jar.

4   The weather was worse on Friday than on Monday.

Superlative adjectives

Superlative adjectives are used to show that one noun is better or worse than all of the others (e.g. the 'most' it can be). The ending of the adjective is usually –est.

Underline the superlative adjective in each sentence.

1   The tallest girl won the high jump competition.

2   There were lots of beautiful girls, but Freya was the prettiest.

3   Of all the creatures on show, the ant was the smallest.

4   Toby received the most pocket money out of everybody.

Writing sentences using different adjectives

Rewrite these sentences, making sure that they contain at least one comparative adjective or superlative adjective.

1   The lion roared at the child.

_____

2   The North Star shines in the sky.

_____

3   Matilda was tall.

_____

Subject–verb agreement

What are subjects?

The subject of a sentence is simply 'who' or 'what' the sentence is about.

Underline the subject in each sentence.

1 The bike is broken.

2 The children are playing happily.

3 Where is my toothbrush?

4 The girl was singing in the rain!

5 The noise was unbearable.

6 The pencils were all missing.

Types of subject

The subject of a sentence can either be singular (one person or object) or plural (more than one person or object).

In the sentences, write (S) next to the singular subjects and (P) next to the plural subjects.

1 The children _____ were excited!

2 The toy _____ sadly ripped in two.

3 The birds _____ flew across the beautiful sky _____.

4 The pen _____ would not write on the glossy paper _____.

Top Tip

Plural subjects often have an 's' on the end to help you identify them. Think carefully about the picture in your head as you read the sentence to see whether it is one item or more than one item being described.

Subject–verb agreement

When a subject is singular in a sentence, the verb is also singular. When a subject is plural, the verb must also be plural.

Rewrite these sentences correctly.

1 The children was happy. _____

2 I are lying on the floor. _____

3 The girl were playing with the toys.

_____

4 Butterflies is pretty when they fly in the garden.

_____

Standard English

Standard English means using the agreed English language with all of its tenses and rules applied correctly.

Rewrite these sentences, making sure the non-standard English mistakes are corrected.

1 I ain't never going.

_____

2 I don't want nothing!

_____

3 The games we played were well cool.

_____

4 If he did waited, he would of been late.

_____

5 He jumped off of the wall.

_____

Formal or informal?

Writing can follow the same set of rules, but can vary in degrees of formality, based on the audience and purpose. For example, a note to a friend will be more informal than a letter of complaint to a shop.

For each sentence, write 'formal' or 'informal' to show which type of writing you would use for each scenario.

1 An e-mail to a pen friend. _____

2 A letter to your head teacher. _____

3 A school report to parents. _____

4 A personal diary entry. _____

5 A postcard to a family member. _____

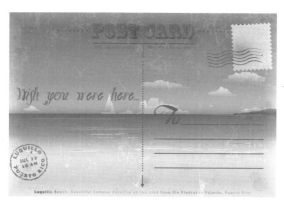

Connectives

What is a connective?

A connective is a word that connects phrases, words, clauses and sentences. Connectives can be used in different places in a sentence.

Underline the connective in each sentence.

1   The balloon flew in the sky and landed in a tree.

2   The children played happily before they all fell out!

3   Although the rain was pouring, the family went for a walk.

4   I ran all the way home because I wanted to play.

5   The pyjamas were snuggly, especially the soft fleece lining.

Top Tip

Connectives help your writing to flow and they prevent you having to write in lots of short sentences. Try to use a variety of connectives throughout your writing.

Different types of connectives

Connectives can be used in different ways including:

• To add information to a sentence

• To sequence information

• To compare information.

In the sentences, write (A) to show if the connective is for addition, (S) for sequencing connectives and (C) for comparing connectives.

1   Finally _____, after a long drive, the family arrived home.

2   As well as _____ the presents under the tree, the children each had a stocking full of presents!

3   The sharks were vicious, similarly _____ so were the catfish.

4   The girl tied her shoes, then _____ she put on her coat.

5   The school had good grades for English, likewise _____ their maths was good too.

6   The robots were advancing on the city, meanwhile _____ the defences were being installed.

Spotting connectives

Underline the connective in each sentence.

1 Jacob likes running, but likes cycling more.

2 Some people do not like olives because of their bitter taste.

3 Vicky likes marshmallows, therefore she bought a big bag of them.

4 After the storm had subsided, the villagers surveyed the damage.

5 As well as breaking his arm, Max broke his leg when he fell from the tree.

Types of connectives

Connectives can be used in different ways:

• **Coordinating** connectives show that both parts of the sentence are equally important.

• **Subordinating** connectives show that one part of the sentence is a subordinate clause.

• **Contrasting** connectives contrast two parts of a sentence with each other.

In the sentences, write (S) to show subordinating connectives, (C) for coordinating connectives and (X) for contrasting connectives.

1 The animals kept running although _____ they were tired.

2 Mark went to the toyshop and _____ bought some Lego.

3 The head teacher was cross because _____ the school was flooded.

4 George fed the fish before _____ he had his dinner.

Types of sentence

Different types of sentences

There are four main types of sentence. Identify each type below using the following code: S (statement), Q (question), C (command) and E (exclamation).

1 When can we have our lunch? ☐

2 Can I go out to play? ☐

3 I am eating my lunch. ☐

4 Don't run in the corridors. ☐

5 Help! ☐

6 My lunch is yummy! ☐

7 I like playing on the beach. ☐

8 Eat your lunch now. ☐

Top Tip

Use the punctuation of a sentence to help you identify its purpose.

Simple sentences

A simple sentence contains one subject and one verb (this is called a clause). In each sentence below, underline the verb and circle the subject.

1 Freya played the piano.

2 Nick mended the window.

3 Claire cooked the dinner.

Compound sentences

A compound sentence has two important clauses. Each clause makes sense on its own, and the clauses are joined with a connective to make a compound sentence.

Use the simple sentences below to make three compound sentences, adding a suitable connective.

Top Tip

To identify a compound sentence, look to see whether the clauses make sense on their own; if they do, the sentence definitely is compound!

The children played.	James liked football.
Tim liked golf.	The adults read.
The sun is shining.	The bees are buzzing.

1 _____

2 _____

3 _____

Complex sentences

A complex sentence has a main clause with one or more subordinate (less important) clauses added to it. A main clause will make sense on its own, but a subordinate clause will not make sense on its own. A main clause can be split in two by a subordinate clause, e.g. The man, *who was nervous*, crossed the rickety bridge.

Rewrite these sentences, adding one or more subordinate clauses to make them complex sentences.

1 The children, ..., hurried to school.

_____

2 Thomas, ..., dreamed of knights and wizards.

_____

3 Harry dried himself off, ...

_____

4 The children, ..., played happily, ...

_____

_____

5 The books in the library, ..., had never been borrowed.

_____

_____

Writing your own sentences

1 Write a simple sentence.

_____

2 Write a compound sentence.

_____

_____

3 Write a complex sentence.

_____

_____

_____

_____

Complex sentences

Every sentence has at least one verb

Underline the verbs in each of these sentences.

1 The train stopped at the station.

2 The news spread quickly.

3 The children played merrily.

4 The monkey yelled at the top of his voice.

5 The woman was late for work.

Main clauses

Underline the main clause in each of these complex sentences.

1 The children, who were all aged 5, loved going to school.

2 The elephant squirted water, because he was naughty!

3 As he shouted at the children, the man went red in the face.

4 Sometimes, when the rain pours from the sky, I get bored.

5 The cows, who were chewing happily on the cud, did not want to be moved from their field.

Top Tip

The main clause would make sense on its own as a simple sentence; it is the main point of the sentence.

Subordinate clauses

Underline the subordinate clause in each of these sentences.

1 The rules of English, and particularly grammar, are difficult to understand.

2 The rope swing, which had a frayed rope, fell from the tree.

3 The museum, which opened late on Saturdays, contained lots of model trains.

4 As the sun shone, the children played in the park.

5 The telephone rang, as the woman slept.

Top Tip

A subordinate clause does not make sense on its own as a simple sentence.

More than one subordinate clause

Sometimes, complex sentences can have more than one subordinate clause. However, they only ever have one main clause.

In each sentence, single underline the first subordinate clause and double underline the second subordinate clause.

1   The woman, who was late, jogged to work, which was only 5 minutes away.

2   It was the middle of January and Father Christmas was in bed with a cold, after his busy Christmas period!

3   The school, that 40 children attended, was closed because the ceiling had collapsed.

4   During the pre-season training, the football coach wanted his players to work harder than before because he wanted to win the cup.

Using subordinate clauses

Write four of your own complex sentences containing two subordinate clauses. In each sentence, circle the main clause, single underline the first subordinate clause and double underline the second subordinate clause.

1   _____

    _____

2   _____

    _____

3   _____

    _____

4   _____

    _____

Prepositions and articles

What is an article?

An article is a word that comes before a noun. There are two types in the English language:

- Definite article (the)
- Indefinite article (a / an)

Circle the articles in these sentences.

1 The apple fell from the tree.

2 A box can make a good castle.

3 The shops will open at 9am.

4 It was time for the wedding to start.

5 It is a good idea to take an umbrella with you.

Adding the correct article

In the sentences, write the correct article to ensure the sentences make sense.

1 _____ swans in _____ garden were beautiful.

2 _____ spaceship is _____ best way to travel to _____ planet.

3 _____ egg is _____ breakfast food.

4 _____ pencils in _____ pot are for all _____ children to use.

5 _____ untidy room is not _____ happy place.

Top Tip

Look carefully at the starting letter of the noun that comes after the article; if it is a vowel it has a different rule.

Prepositions

Prepositions are words that show the relationship of one thing to another.

Underline the prepositions in these sentences.

1 The man jumped over the fence.

2 Children play on the playground.

3 Squirrels live in trees.

4 The boy went under the climbing frame.

5 The directions said to go past the church.

6 Louisa slid down the slide.

Making sure the preposition makes sense

If the wrong preposition is used, the sentence does not make sense.

Rewrite these sentences correctly by changing the preposition.

1   The squirrel climbed under the tree.

   _____

2   I hid over the bushes.

   _____

3   Matilda ran up the classroom.

   _____

4   Leona walked with the path.

   _____

5   The plane flew past the sky.

   _____

6   The girl went under the shop.

   _____

Is it correct?

Tick the sentences that have correct prepositions / articles and cross the sentences that are incorrect.

1   It was the sunny day in a summer holidays.   ☐

2   Freya climbed up the mountain.   ☐

3   The wallet was found under the sofa.   ☐

4   The apple fell from an tree.   ☐

5   It was an August day when a aliens landed!   ☐

6   A happy thing happened to the sisters.   ☐

7   I jogged up the hill and ran past the other side.   ☐

8   An chicken ran across the road.   ☐

Paragraphs

Organising texts

Paragraphs are used to help organise information in a text to make it easier for the reader to follow and understand the events, characters and structure of the text.

Tick the statements that are true about paragraphs.

1   Paragraphs must contain only one sentence. ☐

2   Paragraphs have linking words to the previous or next paragraph. ☐

3   Paragraphs should develop only the topic section, not make links to other paragraphs. ☐

4   Paragraphs can mark a change of setting. ☐

5   Paragraphs always mark a change of setting only. ☐

6   There must be five paragraphs in every piece of writing. ☐

7   Paragraphs can have sub-headings in non-fiction books. ☐

8   Paragraphs start after a line has been missed out. ☐

9   Paragraphs should develop throughout the writing using pronouns, connectives and references to other parts of the text. ☐

10   A new paragraph can be started after an ellipsis in a previous paragraph. ☐

Story structures

All stories have a main structure that consists of five parts.

Label the following (1–5) in order, starting with 1, to show the main structure of all stories.

The middle part of a story should be the most exciting as it is the climax of the action.

Top Tip

Introduction of characters and settings ☐

Events lead towards a resolution ☐

Events lead to a dilemma / problem / issue / main action ☐

Something major happens ☐

Loose ends are resolved ☐

Identifying paragraph breaks

In the following text, mark where the paragraph breaks should go. Use the symbol // to show the breaks.

Once upon a time a little girl called Roxanne lived in a beautiful cottage in the woods with her parents.   She enjoyed all the good things in life and wanted for nothing.   She was surrounded by wildlife and liked nothing better than going for a walk in the forest, talking to the animals and examining the wildlife.   Now, her father and mother always reminded her that she needed to take care and stay away from the Manor House on the other side of the forest.   There were dark stories told about this place and they did not think it was a safe place for little girls.   Roxanne, being only 8 years old and never having been to school, did not understand the dangers of the world.   She had always turned around before reaching the Manor House as her tummy had told her it was time to head home for lunch.   However, on the particular day in question, she had gone for her walk after lunch and therefore had a lot more time on her hands.   Before long she was at the gates of the Manor House.   The gate was rusty and old and one of the hinges had fallen off.   By tugging on the gate, Roxanne found that there was a small girl-shaped hole for her to squeeze through...

Top Tip

Remember, in your own writing you need to plan your paragraphs so that you leave the paragraph breaks rather than adding them in later as an afterthought.

Adding your own paragraph

Continue the story in the box above by writing the next paragraph that you would want to read.

_____

_____

_____

_____

_____

_____

_____

_____

Tense agreement

Why are there different tenses?

The tense that a verb is written in tells the reader whether the action happens in the past, present or future.

For each sentence, write (F) for those sentences that contain the future tense, (P) for the present tense and (X) for the past tense.

1   The car is going to stop.

2   The children had won the cup.

3   We will be leaving for school soon.

4   The man is running to work.

5   The football match has finished.

6   The golf tournament will be finishing soon.

7   The elephants are squirting water.

8   I will go to university one day.

The tense that a verb is written in tells you the time at which the action takes place.

Top Tip

Changing the tense

Write the past and future versions of this sentence.

> I like learning grammar.

Rules of Grammar

Past: _____

Future: _____

Verb tables

Fill in the verb table to show the present, past and future tense of the verb 'to have'. An example has been done for you.

Subject	Present Tense	Past Tense	Future Tense
I	I have	I had	I will have
You			
He / She / It			
We			
They			

Fill in the verb table to show the present, past and future tense of the verb 'to play'.

Subject	Present Tense	Past Tense	Future Tense
I			
You			
He / She / It			
We			
They			

Writing sentences in different tenses

1 Write a simple sentence about a train, in the past tense.

_____

2 Write a compound sentence about a dog, in the present tense.

_____

_____

3 Write a complex sentence about your family, in the future tense.

_____

_____

Active and passive voice

Active voice

When a sentence is written in the active voice, the thing doing the action is the subject.

Underline the subject of each sentence.

1   The cat sat on the mat.

2   Giraffes ate the leaves on the tree.

3   The paper fluttered in the breeze.

4   Miranda revised for her test.

5   The mice ate the cheese.

Passive voice

When a sentence is written in the passive voice, the thing receiving the action becomes the subject.

Underline the subject receiving the action in each sentence.

1   The tree was climbed by the boy.

2   The computer was played on by the man.

3   The stairs were climbed by the girl.

4   The fruit was eaten by the monkey.

5   The walls were painted by the man.

Top Tip

In passive sentences, the thing receiving the action is turned into the subject and the thing doing the action is included near the end, or not at all.

Which is which?

Write (P) for passive voice and (A) for active voice.

1   The children played in the park.

2   The sea was swum in by the sharks.

3   The sharks were entertained by the humans.

4   The man drunk the tea.

5   The bath was run by the lady.

Changing between voices

Rewrite the following sentences in the active voice.

1 The desk was worked at by the businesswoman.

_____

2 The oranges are peeled by the gorillas.

_____

3 Houses are lived in by humans.

_____

4 Adam was carried to school by Jacob.

_____

5 The man was run over by the bike.

_____

Rewrite the following sentences in the passive voice.

6 Vicky ate the chocolate from the tree.

_____

7 The noisy passengers congested the platform.

_____

8 The ice-skater fell onto the ice.

_____

9 The diver explored the shipwreck nervously.

_____

10 The children waved goodbye to their parents.

_____

Using the active and passive voice

1 a) Write a sentence in the active voice.

_____

  b) Write the same sentence as above in the passive voice.

_____

Precision in vocabulary

Standard English

Standard English is when all the rules of English are correctly applied.

Tick the sentences that are coherent (clear and make sense) and use standard English.

1   I should of done that properly. ☐

2   The thing is, if you think about it carefully, the answer is clear. ☐

3   I could have done that even better if I had taken my time. ☐

4   I haven't done nothing wrong! ☐

5   I need to work harder in order to do my best. ☐

Writing concisely

Writing concisely involves choosing words and sentences carefully and not including any unnecessary detail.

Rewrite these sentences in a more concise way.

1   The noisy children who talked lots and make noise in the playground, enjoying playing a whole variety of games.

_____

_____

2   What I meant to say is that I am not really in agreement with the way that the maths has to be taught because I don't agree with it.

_____

_____

3   I don't think that we can agree on this point so we should probably move on so that we can get to the next point which we can debate and hopefully agree on.

_____

_____

_____

Using notes for coherency

You are going to write a short autobiography. Make some brief notes (which may only be bullet points) to help you plan your writing and your paragraphs within it.

Paragraph 1
Paragraph 2
Paragraph 3

Top Tip

It can also be useful to make notes before giving an oral presentation to prevent you hesitating and adding incoherency to your presentation.

Autobiography

Write your short autobiography using the notes you made in the previous exercise. Make sure that you only write the essentials so that it remains coherent throughout.

_____

_____

_____

_____

_____

_____

_____

_____

_____

_____

_____

_____

Full stops, capital letters and more

Full stops and capital letters

Write full stops and capital letters in the passage so that it makes sense.

the cat was playing happily in the streets where he lived the town was called street which was very confusing for the poor postman the cat's name was tiger and his owner was a small boy called tom every morning tiger would sit out on the wall waiting for the postman to deliver the letters to each house and every morning the postman would mumble about how confusing the addresses were

Proper nouns

Proper nouns are names for individual people, places, or organisations. They must have a capital letter at the beginning.

Circle the words that are proper nouns and should have a capital letter.

january	then	james	angry
shop	school	claire	saturday
because	lauren	friday	london

Top Tip

Proper nouns always start with a capital letter wherever they are written in a sentence.

Question marks

Add the correct punctuation to the end of these sentences to show if they are questions or not.

1 Please can I have sandwiches for lunch_____

2 When is it ever going to stop raining_____

3 Is it the end of school yet_____

4 Sandwiches are tasty for my lunch_____

5 The school day is very long, isn't it_____

6 The rain keeps falling from the sky_____

7 Can I learn about other punctuation please_____

Exclamation marks

Write in the exclamation marks and capital letters where they are needed.

1 help help help

2 call an ambulance

3 wow i am so proud of you

4 oh my goodness

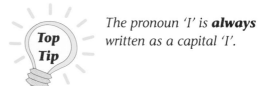

*The pronoun 'I' is **always** written as a capital 'I'.*

Using punctuation correctly

Rewrite this passage, using capital letters, full stops, exclamation marks and question marks correctly.

it was lunchtime at school and the children were drifting slowly into the hall what exciting food was there to eat today the children looked expectantly at the menu board and saw that there was nothing written and no food on the counter oh no the cook explained that the cookers had broken and so there was nothing for the children to eat that day what were they going to do it was a disaster

_____

_____

_____

_____

_____

_____

_____

_____

_____

_____

_____

_____

_____

Commas, colons and semi-colons

Commas in a list

Put the commas in the right places in these lists.

1   The children cut up peppers tomatoes celery cucumber and lettuce.

2   I wanted to buy a huge cuddly happy dog.

3   I went to the shops and bought toothpaste soap rice salt and beans.

4   I have to do my homework wash up and feed the cats before bed.

Commas in sentences

Commas are used to mark a brief pause to help make the meaning of a sentence clearer. Add commas to these sentences, so they make sense.

1   The children who were called Amber and Jake played on the computer.

2   The boy stopped looked at the man and ran on.

3   We waited for ages checked our watches and finally the zoo opened.

4   Nick said "Let's go for a walk in the country."

Top Tip

Commas are used before inverted commas to add a pause before the words are read.

Changing the meaning of a sentence

Commas can dramatically change the meaning of a sentence and therefore need to be used accurately.

Rewrite these sentences by adding or removing commas to change the meaning.

1   After they left Mum, Daisy and Eliza went on the roundabout.

_____

2   When hunting, elephants hide in the undergrowth.

_____

Colons

Colons are used to signal that a list is about to begin or to introduce an explanation. Add colons and commas to the following sentences.

1   Ingredients sugar flour almonds butter.

2   When you get home I would like you to tidy your room hoover the carpet and wash your hair.

3   The kit list said batteries torch sleeping bag wellies and waterproof.

Semi-colons

Level 6

Semi-colons can sometimes be used to replace a full stop as it links two complete sentences that are closely related, making them into one.
Or semi-colons can be used to separate items in a longer list if using commas would be confusing.

Rewrite these sentences as single sentences, using semi-colons.

1   The bus was late. I was going to be late for school.

    _____

2   The school was shut. The water had overflowed from the river and flooded it.

    _____

    _____

3   The police took a long time to come. There was a traffic jam on the main road.

    _____

4   I would like to live somewhere where it snowed lots. I love sledging and building snowmen.

    _____

    _____

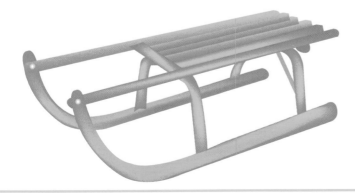

Inverted commas

What is an inverted comma?

Inverted commas are also called speech marks or quotation marks. They are used to show the exact words that someone has spoken. This is also called direct speech.

Write in the missing inverted commas in these sentences.

1   The girl exclaimed, I wish I could fly!"

2   Chan said, "Why do we have to go to school?

3   The teacher was cross and shouted, STOP!

4   I love shopping! announced Josh.

Top Tip

When you finish a sentence, the full stop or punctuation must be inside the final inverted comma, e.g. "Help!"

Direct speech

Direct speech is when the exact words spoken are shown in inverted commas.

Rewrite these sentences as direct speech.

1   Mac asked Tom if he was having a nice day.

_____

2   Tiegan said that she was going to go and hunt for her slippers.

_____

3   Jason shouted loudly that he was very angry with everyone.

_____

4   Mrs Coombs asked the children to close their books and listen to the next instruction.

_____

_____

Reported speech

Reported speech is when the words said are reported, rather than written in inverted commas.

Rewrite these sentences as reported speech.

1 "I am so tired; the baby cried all night long!" moaned Simon.

_____

2 "It is so hot today," said Matthew, "I think I will have an ice-cream."

_____

3 Jack said, "Do I have to climb the beanstalk?"

_____

4 Jack's mum replied, "Yes you do, you lazy boy, and be quick about it!"

_____

Top Tip

When changing direct speech to reported speech, you need to change the word order, and sometimes summarise the words that are said.

Synonyms for 'said'

To keep your writing interesting, when writing about what characters have said, you need to use different words to show how it was said, e.g. 'whispered' is a synonym for 'said'.

Write down ten different words that you could use instead of the word 'said'.

1 _____ **2** _____

3 _____ **4** _____

5 _____ **6** _____

7 _____ **8** _____

9 _____ **10** _____

Apostrophes

Apostrophes for contraction

Apostrophes for contraction are used for words where a letter or letters have been omitted (removed). The apostrophe goes where the letter(s) would be.

Write the common contraction for each of the following words.

1	I am	_____	2	We are _____
3	We have _____		4	It has _____
5	Will not _____		6	They are _____
7	You are _____		8	I have _____
9	I had _____		10	They had _____

Apostrophes for possession

When an apostrophe is used to show possession, it goes after the owner's name to show that it belongs to him / her. For example:

- *The jumper that belonged to the girl* becomes *The girl's jumper.*

Rewrite these phrases to add a possessive apostrophe.

1   The sweets that belong to Max.   _____

2   The computer that belongs to the boy. _____

3   The bike that belongs to Abbie.   _____

4   The blanket that belongs to Tamzin. _____

5   The umbrella that belongs to the man. _____

Apostrophes for possession when words end in 's'

If a word already ends with an 's' and relates to a singular subject, add an apostrophe and then a second 's'. If the word ends in an 's' and relates to a plural subject, put an apostrophe at the end but do not add a second 's'. For example:

- (singular) *James* becomes *James's*

- (plural) *Jones* becomes *Jones'*

Top Tip *Look carefully at the subject of the sentence to see whether it is plural or singular.*

Apostrophes for possession when words end in 's'

Rewrite these sentences adding a possessive apostrophe.

1 The house of the Evans.   _____

2 The bike belonging to Chris.   _____

3 The playground for the girls.   _____

4 The baby of the Campbells.   _____

5 The cars belonged to the boys.   _____

6 The changing room for the ladies. _____

Its or it's?

The word **it's** only ever has an apostrophe when it is used for contraction. If the word **its** is used to show possession it **does not** contain an apostrophe.

Put a tick or cross to show if **its / it's** has been used correctly in these phrases.

1 Its time for dinner! ☐

2 The box and its contents belong to the man. ☐

3 It's almost home time! ☐

4 What is it's name? ☐

5 Its been a really lovely day. ☐

6 I think it's going to rain today. ☐

Using apostrophes

Rewrite these sentences, using apostrophes for contraction or possession.

1 I am very tired today as I have been working hard.

_____

2 The dog ran across the road to the mans house.

_____

3 They looked up happily at the Smiths new house.

_____

4 "They are being a long time!" said Ahmed impatiently.

_____

Brackets and dashes

Why use brackets?

Brackets are used in pairs around a group of words that need to be kept separate within a sentence. The words in the brackets add extra information to the sentence either as an interruption, explanation or afterthought.

Add brackets to these sentences.

1 I have lots of hobbies sewing, painting, reading and cooking which I do regularly.

2 I need some help call me on the telephone to complete my questionnaire.

3 The comma marks a brief pause shorter than a full stop to add meaning to a sentence.

4 The children who were all in Year 6 loved learning about grammar rules.

Top Tip

Brackets can be used to help your writing flow, rather than having lots of separate sentences. Using brackets means you can add information within a sentence without making it too long.

Writing sentences with brackets

1 Write a sentence that uses a set of brackets to contain extra information.

_____

_____

2 Write a sentence that uses a set of brackets to contain a list (like Q1 in the box above).

_____

_____

Double dashes

Double dashes are used, like brackets, to separate a group of words from the rest of the sentence (but only when the words are in the middle of the sentence). The dashes mark a less strong division than brackets.

Add double dashes to the following sentences.

1 The dogs got into line 4 Sheepdogs and 6 Labradors when the judge asked them to.

2 The cars were ready to go all revving their engines on the start line when the lights went out.

3 The children 60 Year 5s were enjoying their residential visit to St Ives.

4 The carnival float belonging to the local committee won the best in the show.

A single dash

A single dash marks an expectant pause or a pause before a change of direction in a sentence.

Rewrite these sentences to contain a single dash.

1 I opened the door a little bit and looked inside. I saw only darkness.

_____

2 The children went for a walk. The footpath crumbled away.

_____

3 The film was full of mistakes. The mistakes could have been avoided.

_____

4 The man paused at the doorway and looked inside. He then ran very fast in the opposite direction.

_____

Hyphens and ellipses

What is a hyphen?

A hyphen is half the length of a dash and it is a linking mark between two words in order to make a new word or expression.

Write a word that can be joined to the word given with a hyphen to make one new word.

1   water- _____

2   ice- _____

3   self- _____

4   twenty- _____

5   X- _____

6   two- _____

7   mid- _____

8   red- _____

9   semi- _____

10 co- _____

Hyphens are useful for linking words that would otherwise end up with two vowels in the middle, e.g. coordinating can become co-ordinating.

The reader fills in the gap

An ellipsis (…) can be used when you want your reader to fill in the details. Finish each of these sentences by adding words and then finishing with an ellipsis.

1   The door _____

2   Through the window _____

3   The air was chilly _____

4   The children _____

5   Smoke drifted _____

Using ellipsis is a good technique when you want to build suspense or mystery in a story.

Using an ellipsis in writing

Write the first paragraph of a mystery story using the starter below. Use at least one ellipsis to add suspense for your reader.

> They had seen the castle many times, but never visited it.

_____

_____

_____

_____

_____

_____

_____

_____

_____

_____

Writing your own

Write your own paragraph, which contains an ellipsis to create tension / suspense.

_____

_____

_____

_____

Full use of punctuation

Which punctuation?

Rewrite these sentences using the correct punctuation.

1 the children were late for school there had been a huge accident on the road

_____

2 i enjoy lots of different sports cycling running high jump and hockey and practise them regularly

_____

3 please can I have my lunch now asked john yes of course replied his mum its beans on toast and apple crumble for pudding

_____

_____

_____

Using a range of punctuation

Write a short paragraph about your favourite hobby or subject at school. Use at least seven different types of punctuation in your writing, including brackets, a semi-colon and a double dash.

_____

_____

_____

_____

_____

_____

_____

_____

_____

_____

_____

_____

_____

Punctuation for understanding

For each sentence, put a cross (✗) if the punctuation is wrong and a tick (✔) if it is correct.

1   I like going to football; lunch will be served at noon. ☐

2   "I need some help please," said Kieran. ☐

3   "Please come and help me." Pleaded Matthew. ☐

4   It is time for lunch (sausage, egg and chips) now. ☐

5   I need: nails; screws; string; wood; and glue. ☐

6   In my picnic I had: plates for the food; cups for the drinks; cutlery to eat with; food to eat; and drinks to drink! ☐

7   I need-ideas to help me understand the work. ☐

8   The water-wheel is working really well. ☐

9   In the competition there were lots of animals – 6 goats, 5 rabbits, 4 chickens and 7 guinea pigs – who all ran riot! ☐

10   Its time for the rabbit to have its tea. ☐

Top Tip

Remember to use a full range of punctuation when you are writing, as this shows that you are using different sentence types, which makes your writing interesting for your reader.

Corrections

Look at your answers for the questions in the box above. Rewrite correctly each sentence that you had identified as being incorrect.

A _____

B _____

C _____

D _____

E _____

Prefixes and suffixes

What is a prefix?

A prefix is a group of letters that can be added to the front of other words to change their meaning.

Circle the correct prefix to change the meaning of these words.

1 **verb**: ad- / anti- / pre-

2 **cycle**: anti- / com-/ tri-

3 **script**: ex- / pro- / post-

4 **act**: anti- / ex- / com-

5 **test**: pro- / post- / tri-

More prefixes

Write a word that can be added to the following prefixes to make a new word. The first line has been done for you.

Prefix	+ word	New word
ab-	duct	abduct
hyper-		
mal-		
in-		
epi-		

Top Tip

Learning the spelling of common prefixes can help you learn to spell lots of new words as you practise common letter strings.

What is a suffix?

A suffix is a group of letters added to the end of a word that change its use.

Circle the suffix that can be added to these words to change them to verbs.

Example: **Travel**: -er / -ful / (-ing)   Verb made: **Travelling**

1 **Help**: -ed / -ship / -ly   Verb made: _____

2 **Work**: -ing / -fully / -less   Verb made: _____

3 **Clean**: -less / -ous / -ing   Verb made: _____

4 **Argue**: -ly / -ed / -ship   Verb made: _____

GRAMMAR

PAGES 4–5 NOUNS AND PRONOUNS

What is a noun?
1 The <u>children</u> jumped.
2 The <u>car</u> was huge.
3 <u>London</u> is big.
4 The <u>dog</u> was tiny.
5 The <u>lion</u> roared.
6 <u>Freya</u> giggled.

What is a pronoun?
1 her; She; her 　 2 his; he 　 3 her; she

Using the correct pronoun
1 They 　 3 they 　 5 me
2 them 　 4 my 　 6 My

Identifying pronouns
1 The coach asked the team to work harder because <u>he</u> wanted <u>them</u> to do <u>their</u> best.
2 The boys stood at the top of the mountain and looked at the beautiful view. <u>They</u> were amazed; <u>it</u> was beautiful.
3 they
4 it

Different types of nouns
1 CM, CM, CL 　 3 CM, AB, CM
2 PR, CM, PR 　 4 CL, CM

PAGES 6–7 VERBS AND ADVERBS

What is a verb?
1 The girl <u>cried</u>
2 The lorry <u>stopped</u>
3 I <u>went</u> to the shops
4 The ant <u>was</u> small
5 The lady <u>smiled</u>
6 Claire <u>worked</u> hard

Verb tenses
1 I walked to school.
2 I ate chips.
3 I learned how to speak French.
4

Subject	Present	Past	Future
I	I run	I ran	I will run
You	You run	You ran	You will run
He/she/it	He/she/it runs	He/she/it ran	She will run
We	We run	We ran	We will run
They	They run	They ran	They will run

What is an adverb?
1 The cup fell <u>gently</u>.
2 The news spread <u>quickly</u>.
3 The children worked <u>hard</u>.
4 The dolphin performed <u>happily</u>.

Adverbs describing adjectives
1 The flowers were (extremely) <u>pretty</u>.
2 The table was (very) <u>heavy</u>.
3 The dress was (completely) <u>ruined</u>.
4 The car was (quite) <u>dirty</u>.

Identifying verbs and adverbs
1 The kind boy (ran) <u>quickly</u> to the shops.
2 The colourful curtains (hung) <u>neatly</u> on the rail.

3 The silent animal (crept) <u>cautiously</u> through the bushes.
4 The noisy car (roared) <u>loudly</u> down the dusty road.

PAGES 8–9 ADJECTIVES

What are adjectives?
1 The <u>bright</u> sun.
2 The <u>short</u> girl.
3 A <u>beautiful</u> baby.
4 The <u>colourful</u> flower.
5 The <u>angry</u> driver.
6 The <u>noisy, smelly</u> car.

Using adjectives in your writing
For example:
1 The <u>happy</u> fish swam in the <u>clean</u> tank.
2 The <u>naughty</u> children played in the <u>spacious</u> park.
3 The <u>noisy</u> lion roared at the <u>scared</u> keeper.

Using exciting adjectives
For example: pleasant; agreeable; kind; friendly; helpful; lovely; tasty; beautiful

Comparative adjectives
1 The beautiful cheetah ran (faster) than the frightened monkey.
2 The pretty flowers were (more) colourful than the prickly shrubs.
3 There were (more) chocolates than sweets in the jar.
4 The weather was (worse) on Friday than on Monday.

Superlative adjectives
1 The <u>tallest</u> girl won the high jump competition.
2 There were lots of beautiful girls, but Freya was the <u>prettiest</u>.
3 Of all the creatures on show, the ant was the <u>smallest</u>.
4 Toby received the <u>most</u> pocket money out of everybody.

Writing sentences using different adjectives
For example:
1 The bravest lion roared at the child.
2 The North Star shines brightest in the sky.
3 Matilda was taller than the other girls in the class.

PAGES 10–11 SUBJECT–VERB AGREEMENT

What are subjects?
1 The <u>bike</u> is broken.
2 The <u>children</u> are playing happily.
3 Where is my <u>toothbrush</u>?
4 The <u>girl</u> was singing in the rain!
5 The <u>noise</u> was unbearable.
6 The <u>pencils</u> were all missing.

Types of subject
1 P 　 2 S 　 3 P; S 　 4 S; S

Subject–verb agreement
1 The children **were** happy.
2 I **am** lying on the floor.
3 The girl **was** playing with the toys.
4 Butterflies **are** pretty when they fly in the garden.

Standard English
1 I **am** never going.
2 I don't want **anything**.
3 The games we played were **great**.
4 If he **had** waited, he would **have** been late.
5 He jumped **off** the wall.

Formal or informal?
1 Informal 　　 4 Informal
2 Formal 　　 5 Informal
3 Formal

1

PAGES 12–13 CONNECTIVES

What is a connective?

1 The balloon flew in the sky <u>and</u> landed in a tree.
2 The children played happily <u>before</u> they all fell out!
3 <u>Although</u> the rain was pouring, the family went for a walk.
4 I ran all the way home <u>because</u> I wanted to play.
5 The pyjamas were snuggly, <u>especially</u> the soft fleece lining.

Different types of connectives

1 S   2 A   3 C   4 S   5 C   6 S

Spotting connectives

1 Jacob likes running, <u>but</u> likes cycling more.
2 Some people do not like olives <u>because</u> of their bitter taste.
3 Vicky likes marshmallows, <u>therefore</u> she bought a big bag of them.
4 <u>After</u> the storm had subsided, the villagers surveyed the damage.
5 <u>As well as</u> breaking his arm, Max broke his leg when he fell from the tree.

Types of connectives

1 X   2 C   3 S   4 C

PAGES 14–15 TYPES OF SENTENCE

Different types of sentences

1 Q   3 S   5 E   7 S
2 Q   4 C   6 E   8 C

Simple sentences

1 (Freya) played the piano.
2 (Nick) mended the window.
3 (Claire) cooked the dinner.

Compound sentences

For example:
1 The children played whilst the adults read.
2 Tim liked golf and James liked football.
3 The sun is shining and the bees are buzzing

Complex sentences

For example:
1 The children, who were late, hurried to school.
2 Thomas, who was asleep in bed, dreamed of knights and wizards.
3 Harry dried himself off, after playing in the water.
4 The children, from Class 6, played happily with the football.
5 The books in the library, on the third floor, had never been borrowed.

Writing your own sentences

For example:
1 I ran to the shops.
2 I ran to the shops and I bought a tin of beans.
3 I ran to the shops, stopping at the park to play on the swings, and bought a tin of beans.

PAGES 16–17 COMPLEX SENTENCES

Every sentence has at least one verb.

1 The train <u>stopped</u> at the station.
2 The news <u>spread</u> quickly.
3 The children <u>played</u> merrily.
4 The monkey <u>yelled</u> at the top of his voice.
5 The woman <u>was</u> late for work.

Main clauses

1 <u>The children</u>, who were all aged 5, <u>loved going to school</u>.

2 <u>The elephant squirted water</u>, because he was naughty!
3 As he shouted at the children, <u>the man went red in the face</u>.
4 <u>Sometimes</u>, when the rain pours from the sky, <u>I get bored</u>.
5 <u>The cows</u>, who were chewing happily on the cud, <u>did not want to be moved from their field</u>.

Subordinate clauses

1 The rules of English, <u>and particularly grammar</u>, are difficult to understand.
2 The rope swing, <u>which had a frayed rope</u>, fell from the tree.
3 The museum, <u>which opened late on Saturdays</u>, contained lots of model trains.
4 <u>As the sun shone</u>, the children played in the park.
5 The telephone rang, <u>as the woman slept</u>.

More than one subordinate clause

1 The woman, <u>who was late</u>, jogged to work, <u>which was only 5 minutes away</u>.
2 <u>It was the middle of January</u> and Father Christmas was in bed with a cold, <u>after his busy Christmas period!</u>
3 The school, <u>that 40 children attended</u>, was closed <u>because the ceiling had collapsed</u>.
4 <u>During the pre-season training</u>, the football coach wanted his players to work harder than before <u>because he wanted to win the cup</u>.

Using subordinate clauses

For example:
* (The rabbits) who all lived in the burrow, (liked to play in the fields) especially on sunny days.
* (The journey) between home and school, (always took a long time) because of the slow trucks.

PAGES 18–19 PREPOSITIONS AND ARTICLES

What is an article?

1 (The) apple fell from (the) tree.
2 (A) box can make (a) good castle.
3 (The) shops will open at 9am.
4 It was time for (the) wedding to start.
5 It is a good idea to take (an) umbrella with you.

Adding the correct article

1 **The** swans in **the** garden were beautiful.
2 **A** spaceship is **the** best way to travel to **a** planet.
3 **The** egg is **a** breakfast food.
4 **The** pencils in **the** pot are for all **the** children to use.
5 **An** untidy room is not **a** happy place.

Prepositions

1 The man jumped <u>over</u> the fence.
2 Children play <u>on</u> the playground.
3 Squirrels live <u>in</u> trees.
4 The boy went <u>under</u> the climbing frame.
5 The directions said to go <u>past</u> the church.
6 Louisa slid <u>down</u> the slide.

Making sure the preposition makes sense

For example:
1 The squirrel climbed **up** the tree.
2 I hid **in** the bushes.
3 Matilda ran **into** the classroom.
4 Leona walked **along** the path.
5 The plane flew **in** the sky.
6 The girl went **into** the shop.

Is it correct?

1 X   3 ✔   5 X   7 X
2 ✔   4 X   6 ✔   8 X

PAGES 20–21 PARAGRAPHS

Organising texts

The following should be ticked: 2; 4; 7; 8; 9; 10

Story structures

Introduction of characters and settings – 1

Events lead towards a resolution – 4

Events lead to a dilemma/problem/issue/main action – 2

Something major happens – 3

Loose ends are resolved – 5

Identifying paragraph breaks

There should be a paragraph break after the following sentences:

She was surrounded by wildlife and liked nothing better than going for a walk in the forest, talking to the animals and examining the wildlife. //

There were dark stories told about this place and they did not think it was a safe place for little girls. //

She had always turned around before reaching the Manor House as her tummy had told her it was time to head home for lunch. //

Adding your own paragraph

For example:

Looking left and right along the road and seeing nobody, Roxanne squeezed her way through the hole. A thread from her coat caught on the gate and as she came out the other side, it began to unravel very slowly. Roxanne looked up at the big house and thought how dark and gloomy it looked. At that moment, she heard a sound to her right; it sounded like an animal in distress. She set off to try and help the poor creature.

PAGES 22–23 TENSE AGREEMENT

Why are there different tenses?

1 F	3 F	5 X	7 P
2 X	4 P	6 F	8 F

Changing the tense

PAST: I liked learning grammar.

FUTURE: I will like learning grammar.

Verb tables

Subject	Present Tense	Past Tense	Future Tense
I	I have	I had	I will have
You	You have	You had	You will have
He/she/it	He/she/it has	He/she/it had	He/she/it will have
We	We have	We had	We will have
They	They have	They had	They will have

Subject	Present Tense	Past Tense	Future Tense
I	I play	I played	I will play
You	You play	You played	You will play
He/she/it	He/she/it plays	He/she/it played	He/she/it will play
We	We play	We played	We will play
They	They play	They played	They will play

Writing sentences in different tenses

For example:

1 The train whistled through the station.

2 The dog is playing in the garden and he is hiding his bone.

3 My family is going on holiday to Spain, because they love it there.

PAGES 24–25 ACTIVE AND PASSIVE VOICE

Active voice

1 The <u>cat</u> sat on the mat.

2 <u>Giraffes</u> ate the leaves on the tree.

3 The <u>paper</u> fluttered in the breeze.

4 <u>Miranda</u> revised for her test.

5 The <u>mice</u> ate the cheese.

Passive voice

1 The <u>tree</u> was climbed by the boy.

2 The <u>computer</u> was played on by the man.

3 The <u>stairs</u> were climbed by the girl.

4 The <u>fruit</u> was eaten by the monkey.

5 The <u>walls</u> were painted by the man.

Which is which?

1 A	2 P	3 P	4 A	5 P

Changing between voices

1 The businesswoman worked at the desk.

2 The gorillas peeled the oranges.

3 Humans live in houses.

4 Jacob carried Adam to school.

5 The bike ran the man over.

6 The chocolate from the tree was eaten by Vicky.

7 The platform was congested by the noisy passengers.

8 The ice was fallen onto by the ice-skater.

9 The shipwreck was explored by the nervous diver.

10 The parents were waved goodbye to by their children.

Using the active and passive voice

For example:

1 a) I ate the cake with my fork.

   b) My fork was used to eat the cake.

PAGES 26–27 PRECISION IN VOCABULARY

Standard English

The following should be ticked: 2, 3 and 5

Writing concisely

For example:

1 The noisy children enjoyed playing a variety of games in the playground.

2 I am not in agreement with how maths is taught.

3 We can't agree on the first point so let's move to the second.

Using notes for coherency

For example:

Paragraph 1:	
• Name	• Age
• Where I live	• Family

Paragraph 2:
• School – which school and favourite subject: PE
• Hobbies and interests – cycling, reading

Paragraph 3:
• Achievements so far
• Hopes for the future

Autobiography

The answer will be individual to the child, but it needs to be coherent and clearly organized into three paragraphs.

PUNCTUATION

PAGES 28–29 FULL STOPS, CAPITAL LETTERS AND MORE

Full stops and capital letters

The cat was playing happily in the streets where he lived. The town was called Street, which was very confusing for the poor postman. The cat's name was Tiger and his owner was a small boy called Tom. Every morning Tiger would sit out on the wall waiting for the postman to deliver the letters to each house and every morning the postman would mumble about how confusing the addresses were.

Proper nouns

The following words should be circled: january; james; claire; saturday; lauren; friday; london

Question marks

1   Please can I have sandwiches for lunch?
2   When is it ever going to stop raining?
3   Is it the end of school yet?
4   Sandwiches are tasty for my lunch.
5   The school day is very long, isn't it?
6   The rain keeps falling from the sky.
7   Can I learn about other punctuation please?

Exclamation marks

1   Help! Help! Help!
2   Call an ambulance!
3   Wow! I am so proud of you.
4   Oh my goodness!

Using punctuation correctly

It was lunchtime at school and the children were drifting slowly into the hall. What exciting food was there to eat today? The children looked expectantly at the menu board and saw that there was nothing written and no food on the counter! Oh no! The cook explained that the cookers had broken and so there was nothing for the children to eat that day. What were they going to do? It was a disaster!

PAGES 30–31 COMMAS, COLONS AND SEMI-COLONS

Commas in a list

1   The children cut up peppers, tomatoes, celery, cucumber and lettuce.
2   I wanted to buy a huge, cuddly, happy dog.
3   I went to the shops and bought toothpaste, soap, rice, salt and beans.
4   I have to do my homework, wash up and feed the cats before bed.

Commas in sentences

1   The children, who were called Amber and Jake, played on the computer.
2   The boy stopped, looked at the man, and ran on.
3   We waited for ages, checked our watches, and finally the zoo opened.
4   Nick said, "Let's go for a walk in the country."

Changing the meaning of a sentence

1   After they left, Mum, Daisy and Eliza went on the roundabout.
2   When hunting elephants, hide in the undergrowth.

Colons

1   Ingredients: sugar, flour, almonds, butter.
2   When you get home I would like you to: tidy your room, hoover the carpet, and wash your hair.
3   The kit list said: batteries, torch, sleeping bag, wellies and waterproof.

Semi-colons

For example:

1   The bus was late; I was going to be late for school.
2   The school was shut; the water had overflowed from the river and flooded it.
3   The police took a long time to come; there was a traffic jam on the main road.
4   I would like to live somewhere where it snowed lots; I love sledging and building snowmen.

PAGES 32–33 INVERTED COMMAS

What is an inverted comma?

1   The girl exclaimed, "I wish I could fly!"
2   Chan said, "Why do we have to go to school?"
3   The teacher was cross and shouted, "STOP!"
4   "I love shopping!" announced Josh.

Direct speech

For example:

1   "Are you having a nice day Tom?" asked Mac.
2   "I am going to go and hunt for my slippers," announced Tiegan.
3   "I am very angry with EVERYONE!" shouted Jason.
4   "Close your books and listen to the next instruction please," said Mrs Coombs to the children.

Reported speech

For example:

1   Simon said that he was tired because the baby had cried all night long.
2   Matthew said he was going to have an ice-cream because it was so hot.
3   Jack asked whether he had to climb the beanstalk.
4   Jack's mum told him that he did have to and that he needed to stop being lazy and be quick about it.

Synonyms for 'said'

For example: mumbled, answered, questioned, mentioned, asked, replied, inquired, shouted, queried, commanded, cried.

PAGES 34–35 APOSTROPHES

Apostrophes for contraction

1	I'm	5	Won't	9	I'd
2	We're	6	They're	10	They'd
3	We've	7	You're		
4	It's	8	I've		

Apostrophes for possession

1   Max's sweets.
2   The boy's computer.
3   Abbie's bike.
4   Tamzin's blanket.
5   The man's umbrella.

Apostrophes for possession when words end in 's'

1   The Evans' house.
2   Chris's bike.
3   The girls' playground.
4   The Campbells' baby.
5   The boys' cars.
6   The ladies' changing room.

Its or it's?

1	✗	2	✓	3	✓	4	✗	5	✗	6	✓

Using apostrophes

1   I'm very tired today as I've been working hard.
2   The dog ran across the road to the man's house.

3   They looked up happily at the Smiths' new house.

4   "They're being a long time!" said Ahmed impatiently.

PAGES 36–37 BRACKETS AND DASHES

Why use brackets?

1   I have lots of hobbies (sewing, painting, reading and cooking) which I do regularly.

2   I need some help (call me on the telephone) to complete my questionnaire.

3   The comma marks a brief pause (shorter than a full stop) to add meaning to a sentence.

4   The children (who were all in Year 6) loved learning about grammar rules.

Writing sentences with brackets

For example:

1   There are lots of children in the school (more boys than girls though).

2   I like doing art (painting, drawing, sketching and colouring), particularly when it is messy!

Double dashes

1   The dogs got into line – 4 Sheepdogs and 6 Labradors – when the judge asked them to.

2   The cars were ready to go – all revving their engines on the start line – when the lights went out.

3   The children – 60 Year 5s – were enjoying their residential visit to St Ives.

4   The carnival float – belonging to the local committee – won the best in the show.

A single dash

1   I opened the door a little bit and looked inside – I saw only darkness.

2   The children went for a walk – the footpath crumbled away.

3   The film was full of mistakes – the mistakes could have been avoided.

4   The man paused at the doorway and looked inside – he then ran very fast in the opposite direction.

PAGES 38–39 HYPHENS AND ELLIPSES

What is a hyphen?

For example:

1	water-wheel	6	two-thirds
2	ice-skate	7	mid-air
3	self-worth	8	red-hot
4	twenty-five	9	semi-colon
5	X-ray	10	co-ordinate

The reader fills in the gap

For example:

1   The door creaked open slowly…

2   Through the window the outline of a big, black dog was looming…

3   The air was chilly and the shadow moved…

4   The children were in trouble now…

5   Smoke drifted slowly up the chimney and the bird in the nest…

Using an ellipsis in writing

For example:

They had seen the castle many times, but never visited it. The stories they had heard about it had been enough to stop them ever wanting to step foot in it. That had been easy until now as the door had been firmly closed. Today it was ajar… The children looked at each other, their looks daring each other to enter the castle. At last, Max said, "Come on! What's the worst that can happen?" The others kept their answers to themselves but nevertheless entered the castle…

Writing your own

Accept children's own answer.

PAGES 40–41 FULL USE OF PUNCTUATION

Which punctuation?

1   The children were late for school; there had been a huge accident on the road.

2   I enjoy lots of different sports (cycling, running, high jump and hockey) and practise them regularly.

3   "Please can I have my lunch now?" asked John. "Yes of course," replied his mum, "it's beans on toast, and apple crumble for pudding."

Using a range of punctuation

Children's own answers, but answers need to include a set of brackets, a semi-colon, double dashes and four other types of punctuation.

Punctuation for understanding

1	✗	3	✗	5	✗	7	✗	9	✔
2	✔	4	✔	6	✔	8	✔	10	✗

Corrections

A   I like going to football. Lunch will be served at noon.

B   "Please come and help me!" pleaded Matthew.

C   I need: nails, screws, string, wood and glue.

D   I need ideas to help me understand the work.

E   It's time for the rabbit to have its tea.

SPELLING

PAGES 42–43 PREFIXES AND SUFFIXES

What is a prefix?

1   ad-   2   tri-   3   post-   4   ex-   5   pro-

More prefixes

For example:

Prefix	+ word	New word
ab-	duct	abduct
hyper-	tension	hypertension
mal-	nutrition	malnutrition
in-	accurate	inaccurate
epi-	centre	epicentre

What is a suffix?

1	-ed; Helped	2	-ing; Working
3	-ing; Cleaning	4	-ed; Argued

Words ending in 'l'

1	identically	2	schooling
3	soulfully	4	beautifully
5	ailment	6	pencilled

Words ending in 'e'

Root word	+ -ing	+ -ed
hope	hoping	hoped
love	loving	loved

Root word	+ -ing	+ -ed
shame	shaming	shamed
make	making	✗
shake	shaking	✗
assume	assuming	assumed
take	taking	✗

PAGES 44–45 MORE COMPLEX PREFIXES AND SUFFIXES

What is a more complex prefix?

1 ir- 2 il- 3 ad- 4 ad- 5 ac-

More prefixes

For example:

1 abnormal, absent, aboriginal
2 antivirus, antifreeze, antidote
3 illuminate, illegal, illogical
4 affirm, affair, affluent
5 approve, appear, appoint,

Complex suffixes

For example:

Noun	Suffix to add	Verb
book	-ed	booked
terror	-ise	terrorise
advert	-ise	advertise
liquid	-ate	liquidate
critic	-ise	criticise
pace	-ify	pacify
toxic	-ate	toxicate
central	-ise	centralise
broad	-en	broaden

Complex prefix or suffix?

1 legal(ity) 5 not(ify)
2 class(ify) 6 (il)legal(ity)
3 (in)toxic(ate) 7 (il)luminate
4 (ad)journ 8 (anti)freeze

PAGES 46–47 VOWELS AND CONSONANTS

What are the vowels?

A	E	I	O	U

Consonants

For example:

A consonant is a letter that is not a vowel. A consonant can be added to a vowel to form a syllable.

Spot the vowel sound

1 (o)ver 6 c(a)t
2 c(o)nc(e)rn 7 sw(i)m
3 thro(ug)h 8 (u)mbr(e)ll(a)
4 fl(y) 9 (u)n(i)f(y)
5 rel(y) 10 cr(i)(e)d

Spotting consonants

The following should be circled: endless; suspect; trouble; needless; when; Mississippi

Consonants making different sounds

For example:

Making the sound 'h'	Not making the sound 'h'
hair	hour
history	honour
happen	heir
hate	vehicle
hard	Sarah
heard	honest

For example:

Making the sound 'g'	Making the sound 'j'	Making the sound 'zh'
gap	agent	beige
gawp	suggestion	rouge
gain	energy	prestige
guess	huge	mirage
against	manager	collage

PAGES 48–49 HOMOPHONES AND HOMONYMS

What are homophones?

1 pour 4 reigned 7 flour
2 their 5 too 8 pairs
3 great 6 They're

Alternative homophones

1 stairs 5 meddle 9 hare
2 where 6 fourth 10 read
3 heir 7 blew
4 tale 8 beech

What are homonyms?

For example:

1 the action of moving ones hand from side to side in greeting
2 a wooden implement used to hit the ball in cricket
3 a timepiece that usually fits around the wrist
4 a metal band that is worn on the finger

Spot the homonyms and homophones

1 Kangaroos often live in Australia. (There) legs are long and extend to help them jump long distances. That is why they are good jumpers.
2 The children were going on a school trip. The coach was going to drive them to the museum (wear) they would have a (grate) time!
3 The tennis match was going to be between the two best players. They had worked hard to improve (there) game. They (staired) at each other from across the (caught).

PAGES 50–51 SPELLING STRATEGIES 1

Words within words

1 create 3 definite 5 sphere
2 encounter 4 smartly 6 hearty

Syllable hunting

For example:

1 vo-cab-u-la-ry
2 sat-is-fy
3 ex-agg-er-ate
4 ex-pla-na-tion
5 sim-i-lar

PAGES 52–53 SPELLING STRATEGIES 2

Mnemonics

For example:

1 Daring, Excited Beavers Are Terrorising Everything
2 Brave Ruthless Umbrellas Irritate Sunshine Everywhere
3 Kangaroos Never Eat Any Dung
4 Sometimes I Get Naughty
5 Yoghurt And Chocolate Hate Trolls
6 Elegant Queens Usually Ignore Pigs

PAGES 54–55 WORD FAMILIES, ROOTS AND ORIGINS

Identify the root words

1 aquarium 4 geography 7 transport
2 biology 5 reject 8 zoology
3 democracy 6 sympathy

Word families using roots

For example:

1. transport, portable, report
2. neurology, neuroscience, neuron
3. geology, geography, geothermal
4. equality, equity, equate

Match the origin

aqua – water min – small
demo – people morph – form
loc – place zoo – animal

Word families and meanings

For example:

1. multitask; multiply; multiplication
2. archangel; monarch; archenemy
3. chromatic; monochrome; polychrome
4. credible; credit; incredible
5. equation; equally; equity
6. paternal; patriotic; paternity
7. vocation; vocational; vocal
8. spectacles; spectator; prospect.

PAGES 56–57 MORE COMPLEX WORD FAMILIES

Form-based families

For example:

1. word – wordy – wordless – wording
2. teach – teacher – teaching – unteachable
3. final – finally – finale – finality
4. improve – improvement – improving – improved
5. behave – behaviour – behaving – behavioural
6. book – bookworm – bookshelf – bookseller

Word-webs

For example:

psychology, biology, technology, sociology, ideology, apology, geology, ecology, chronology, anthology, phonology, meteorology, pharmacology, zoology

Meaning-based families

For example:

1. education, learning, teaching, students, pupils, headteacher, educating, mathematics
2. animal, warm-blooded, hair, fur, milk, human, legs, reproduction
3. eating, vegetables, fruit, chew, swallow, taste, dinner, lunch
4. patients, doctors, surgeons, illness, injury, plasters, cleanliness, remedy

Word-webs

For example:

writing, pencil, ball-point, fountain pen, script, literacy, books, communication

PAGES 58–59 INFLECTIONAL ENDINGS

What is an inflectional ending?

Root word	+ er	+ ing	+ed
travel	traveller	travelling	travelled
walk	walker	walking	walked
amble	ambler	ambling	ambled
clap	clapper	clapping	clapped
milk	milker	milking	milked

Changes to the root word

1. creation

For example: remove the final e of the root word and add the inflectional ending.

2. wrestling

For example: remove the final e of the root word and add the inflectional ending.

3. easiest

For example: remove the final y of the root word, add 'i' and add the inflectional ending.

4. collectivism

For example: remove the final e of the root word and add the inflectional ending.

5. trapping

For example: double the final consonant and add the inflectional ending.

6. hopped

For example: double the final consonant and add the inflectional ending.

Further examples

For example:

1. absolute = absolution, activate = activation, decorate = decoration, estimate = estimation…
2. examine = examining, give = giving, like = liking…
3. sandy = sandiest, grassy = grassiest, busy = busiest
4. active = activism, future = futurism…
5. wrap = wrapping, hop = hopping, shop = shopping…
6. pop = popped, stop = stopped, crop = cropped…

PAGES 60–61 EDITING SKILLS

Spelling and punctuation errors

For example:

It was a cold, windy and wet day in the middle of February. The ground was wet from the rain that had fallen non-stop for several days. James was sitting in his room feeling fed up; he just wanted to be able to go out and play on his new bike.

Repetition of words

The following should be underlined:

I was so excited about the weekend because I was going to be the carnival princess. I was chosen because I won the competition in the local paper. I was going to wear a beautiful gold dress with a beautiful tiara and beautiful silver shoes. I was going to look beautiful. My excitement disappeared when I looked at the weather.

Example of a rewritten answer:

I had been excited about the weekend as I was going to be the carnival princess. I'd been chosen because I had won the competition in the local paper. The dress I was to wear was long and beautiful with a glittering tiara and sparkly silver shoes. I was so excited as I was going to look gorgeous. However, when I looked at the weather, my excitement evaporated.

Sentences making sense

The door creaked open and all I could see was darkness. Before my eyes could become accustomed to the dark there was a loud bang. I looked left and right. What was I to do? The door had swung shut behind me. I was trapped. The sounds began again; I put my hands over my ears. I curled up small and hoped that someone, anyone would come and rescue me.

Editing a piece of writing

For example:

I went to Spain on holiday and had a wonderful time; the weather was amazing. The hotel I stayed in was huge and full of very friendly people. Whilst I was away I surprised myself by trying lots of different foods and, amazingly, enjoyed all of them!

As well as the tasty food and beautiful weather, I took part in a range of exciting activities. By doing this, I met lots of new people and have made some friendships for life. I particularly enjoyed the paragliding because it was very special to be up so high, like a bird. On the other hand, I did not enjoy the jet-ski ride as it scared me when it went so fast.

Surprisingly, we did have one day of rain (a freak storm apparently), but that did not dampen my holiday as I stayed in the hotel and went to the brilliant indoor pool. I would definitely recommend Spain as a holiday destination; I will certainly be going back again!

VOCABULARY

PAGES 62–63 ANTONYMS AND SYNONYMS

What are synonyms?

For example:

1   whispered, asked, stated
2   glad, excited, content
3   good, great, entertaining
4   lovely, enjoyable, wonderful
5   extremely, particularly, tremendously

Enhancing writing with synonyms

For example:

I went on the swings at the park and had fun. I also went down the slide, which was amazing! The roundabout was cool as well! I enjoyed myself at the park as it was a hot, sunny day. I'd love to have another fantastic time at the park when the weather is warm again.

Antonyms

1	sad	5	shallow	9	young / new
2	wet	6	late	10	ugly
3	cold	7	go		
4	light	8	short		

Using antonyms in writing

For example:

1   The cold toast tasted good!
2   The pretty frog kissed the ugly princess.
3   The fast fish darted along the fast moving river.
4   The sad child played with the hard teddy.
5   The old teacher was excited to meet her good class.

PAGES 64–65 SPEECH VOCABULARY

Which type of speech?

1   D   2   D   3   R   4   D   5   R

Using correct speech punctuation

For example:

"We are going on a visit to a science museum at the end of the month," Miss Dawson told her class.

"Rubbish, a pitch black cave would be better than that," moaned Daniel.

"Where is the museum, Miss?" asked Ryan.

"A good question Ryan, it is in London," Miss Dawson replied.

"Great, I'll end up being sick on the bus, I always get travel sick on long journeys," sobbed Sarah.

"Well, I've been before and it is brilliant, I can't wait to go again with all my friends," said Freya excitedly.

"I'd like to find out more about how the Earth was formed and there'll be stuff about that there," exclaimed Joe with pleasure.

"Well I wish I could go anywhere else in the world but there," mumbled Daniel again.

"Please can we have some order," pleaded Miss Dawson, "so I can tell you more about the visit?   You will be split

into small groups so that you can see the exhibits better."

Daniel grunted, "I'll probably end up in her group because I always have to go with the teacher."

Miss Dawson silenced him with a glare.

Ryan whispered, "Sam, I hope I'm in your group."

"I want to be in your group Georgia," whispered Freya.

"Jacob, we could be in a group together," shouted Joe, right across the room. Miss Dawson raised her head above the din and shouted, "STOP! I think it would be best if we just cancel the visit altogether!"

PAGES 66–67 SINGULAR AND PLURAL

What does singular and plural mean?

1	plural	4	singular
2	singular	5	plural
3	plural	6	plural

Words ending in 's' when they are singular

1	buses	4	witnesses
2	fortresses	5	gases
3	kisses		

Singular words ending in 'y'

1	ponies	4	spies
2	days	5	puppies
3	canaries	6	fairies

Singular words ending in 'f'

| 1 | loaves | 3 | wolves |
| 2 | shelves | 4 | halves |

Singular words ending in 'o'

1	videos	4	heroes
2	echoes	5	mangoes
3	volcanoes	6	dominoes

PAGES 68–69 TECHNICAL VOCABULARY

What is technical vocabulary?

Technical vocabulary is subject-specific vocabulary. It is often found in non-fiction books where difficult concepts are explained. These books contain a glossary where the definition of the technical words is given.

Where would you find technical vocabulary?

The following words should be circled: newspaper; non-chronological reports; report texts; recipes

Spot the technical vocabulary

Microscopes have played a large part in the understanding of medicine. They allow researchers to examine microscopic items in a huge amount of detail. The magnification can be changed and adapted based on the specimen being examined. Scientists have made huge breakthroughs and will continue to do so with the help of some equipment.

Using technical vocabulary in sentences

1   scientists
2   telescope, astronomers

3   evaporation
4   lava, erupts

Using technical vocabulary

Children's own answers but technical vocabulary must be specific to the topic.

PAGE 70–71 FIGURATIVE LANGUAGE

Personification

1   The snowman …is a chubby boy wrapped up warm.
2   Summer … is a woman with long golden hair
3   The storm … ran wild among the trees.
4   Fire … swallowed the houses.
5   The sun … glared down from the sky.
6   The ocean … danced in the moonlight.

Alliteration

For example:

1   Wind whistles wildly.
2   Big, black, bold beetles.
3   Seven seals sit sullenly and silently on the sand.
4   Ten tractors trudge tentatively towards the town.
5   Fish flip ferociously.

Assonance

1   A   3   A   5   A
2   L   4   A   6   L

Onomatopoeia

For example:

POW!   WHAM!   SLURP!   CRASH!
BAM!   ZOOOOM!   BIFF!
BOOM!   POP!   SOK!

Which is which?

1   P   3   O   5   P
2   L   4   A   6   O

PAGES 72–73 PERSONAL FORM AND IMPERSONAL FORM

What is the impersonal language form?

1   ✗   2   ✔   3   ✗   4   ✗   5   ✔   6   ✔

When is it used?

The following words should be circled: legal document; information text; balanced argument

Formal or informal?

1   F   3   F   5   F   7   I
2   F   4   I   6   F   8   F

Writing formally and impersonally

Children's own answers but they must be written in formal, impersonal language.

Writing informally

The same paragraph as above but using informal style.

TEST PRACTICE

PAGE 74

1   "Stop"   [1 mark]
    ✔

2   The children **were** playing in the park.
    Today, Simon **is** still Tom's best friend.
    The baby **was** crying very loudly!
                [1 mark: award 1 mark for all 3 correct]

3   a)   imogen went to london in may to see her friend
                [1 mark: award 1 mark for all 3 correct]

    b)   Example: Imogen OR London OR May
         It is a proper noun OR It is a name or month
                                                 [2 marks]

4

Word from the sentence	Noun	Verb	Pronoun
watched		✔	
elephant	✔		
They			✔
stayed		✔	

                [1 mark: award 1 mark for all 4 correct]

5   Example: enjoyable OR agreeable OR pleasant OR tasty
    OR good OR lovely…   [1 mark]

PAGES 75–76

1   The thief ran across the road and the car swerved into
    the tree.   [1 mark: award 1 mark for both correct]

2   have   ✔   [1 mark]

3   Today it was raining **however** it had been sunny the day
    before. Jason **and** Ross were glad that they had tested

their rocket yesterday **otherwise** they would not have
been able to see it work at all.
                [1 mark: award 1 mark for all 3 correct]

4   Paragraphs can signal a change of action   ✔
    Paragraphs help to organise longer texts   ✔
                [1 mark: award 1 mark for both correct]

5   It's been a lovely day and the dog enjoyed its walk
    ✔   [1 mark]

6   The children, who were all in the same class, visited
    the swimming pool.
                [1 mark: award 1 mark for both commas correct]

7   elephant – B   squirted – D
    happily – C   angry – A
                [1 mark: award 1 mark for all 4 correct]

8

	Main clause	Subordinate clause
The boys, who were all nine, **swam across the pool.**	✔	
The roof collapsed because of the weight of snow.	✔	
The lady ran quickly, **because she was late.**		✔
The teacher, who was called Claire, **worked extremely hard all day.**	✔	

                [2 marks: award 2 marks for all 4 correct,
                award 1 mark for 2 of the 3 correct]

9

9   Example: Eliza stated, "I am going to work much harder at grammar from now on."

[1 mark: no mark given if the full stop is outside the inverted commas]

10 light   **[1 mark]**

PAGES 77–78

1   <u>The</u> children walked to school.
It was sunset and time for <u>the</u> school to be locked up.
Jasmine looked up and <u>an</u> apple fell from <u>the</u> tree above her.

[1 mark: award 1 mark for all 3 correct]

2   The prize, a glittering gold cup, stood on the table at the front.   ✔
The nosiest girl, whose name was Karen, did not win the prize.   ✔

[1 mark: award 1 mark for both correct]

3   ponies   ✔   **[1 mark]**

4   (After) the earthquake, the buildings were destroyed.   **[1 mark]**

5   The birds <u>flew</u> over the house.
I <u>was</u> good at my grammar test.

[2 marks: award 1 mark for each correct answer to a total of 2 marks]

6   The girl from across the road (who is also my friend) was not very well.   ✔   **[1 mark]**

7   water – wheel; red – hot; twenty – three

[1 mark: award 1 mark for all 3 correct]

8   a)   brackets   **[1 mark]**
    b)   To separate a group of words in a sentence   ✔   **[1 mark]**

9   I had to pack: six shirts – colon; The door creaked open slowly… – ellipsis; The ninety-nine bottles sat on the wall – hyphen;

[1 mark: award 1 mark for all 3 correct]

PAGE 79

1   pears
    great   **[2 marks: award 1 mark for each correct answer to a total of 2 marks]**

2   <u>anti</u>-virus   <u>un</u>-happy
    <u>mal</u>-nutrition

[1 mark: award 1 mark for all 3 correct]

3   their   ✔   **[1 mark]**

4   Example: transport, portable, transportation, airport, deport, export, import, passport…

[1 mark: award 1 mark for 3 correct words]

5   (hurried)   **[1 mark]**

PAGE 80

The following are the correct spellings:

1	thought	6	imagine
2	disappointed	7	tomorrow
3	hopping	8	create
4	terminate	9	investigate
5	too	10	bookmark

**[Each correctly spelt word should be awarded 1 mark
Do *not* award a mark for the following:**

• **If more than one attempt has been given, but it is not clear which attempt your child wants to be marked.**

• **If the word has been correctly spelt but the word has been split into clearly divided components.**

• **If the word has been spelt correctly but an apostrophe or hyphen has been inserted.]**

PAGE 81

1   The boy broke the window.   ✔   **[1 mark]**

2   Example: the dirty car on the driveway   **[1 mark]**

3   The team is playing well in their football match and is winning the game.   **[1 mark]**

4

Noun	Abstract	Collective	Common	Proper
a flock		✔		
Cambridge				✔
glass			✔	
hope	✔			

[1 mark: award 1 mark for all 4 correct]

5   (trains)
    (is)
    (have)

[1 mark: award 1 mark for all 3 correct]

PAGE 82

1

	un-	dis-	de-
respect		✔	
helpful	✔		
classify			✔

[1 mark: award 1 mark for all 3 correct]

2   terror-<u>ise</u>   **[1 mark]**

3   pre<u>scrip</u>tion
    transpor<u>ta</u>tion
    multipli<u>ca</u>tion

[1 mark: award 1 mark for all 3 correct]

4   Example: through, though, thought, ought, trough, thorough…   **[1 mark]**

5   (jewellery)   **[1 mark]**

PAGE 83

The following are the correct spellings:

1	receipt	6	doubt
2	questionnaire	7	business
3	broccoli	8	woollen
4	citizen	9	dictionary
5	seize	10	suspicious

[Each correctly spelt word should be awarded 1 mark

Do *not* award a mark for the following:

• **If more than one attempt has been given, but it is not clear which attempt your child wants to be marked.**

• **If the word has been correctly spelt but the word has been split into clearly divided components.**

• **If the word has been spelt correctly but an apostrophe or hyphen has been inserted.**

PAGE 84

The responses will vary, but there are a total of 14 marks available for this task. The marks will be broken up as follows:

Up to 6 marks for 'Sentence structure and punctuation':

- Range of grammatical structures, e.g. complex sentences, deliberate control of verbs, complex verb phrases, impersonal constructions.
- Appropriate range of punctuation, including internal sentence punctuation (e.g. semi-colons, commas)

Up to 4 marks for 'Text structure and organisation':

- Structure controlled and links between paragraphs in a variety of ways.
- Paragraphs varied, e.g. single sentence to secure argument, movement of focus from general to specific.
- Evidence of cohesive devices within paragraphs, e.g. contrast and repetition.

Up to 4 marks for 'Appropriateness and vocabulary':

- Text adapted for the leaflet, addressing the specified audience, focused on purpose
- Ambitious vocabulary choices.

SPELLING TASK ADMINISTRATION

The instructions below are for the spelling tasks (levels 3–5 page 80, and level 6 page 83).
Read the following instruction out to your child:

I am going to read 10 sentences out to you. Each sentence has a word missing. Listen carefully to the missing word and fill this in the answer space, making sure that you spell it correctly
I will read the word, then the word within the sentence, and then I will repeat the word for a third time.

You should now read the spellings 3 times, as given below. Leave at least a 12-second gap between spellings. At the end, read all 10 sentences again, giving your child the chance to make any changes they wish to their answers.

PAGE 80 SPELLING TASK LEVELS 3–5

1 **Spelling one**: the word is **thought**.
The boy **thought** about the answer.
The word is **thought**.

2 **Spelling two**: the word is **disappointed**.
She was **disappointed** with her test result.
The word is **disappointed**.

3 **Spelling three**: the word is **hopping**.
The children were **hopping** in the playground.
The word is **hopping**.

4 **Spelling four**: the word is **terminate**.
The train would **terminate** at the station.
The word is **terminate**.

5 **Spelling five**: the word is **too**.
It was **too** long for the children to wait.
The word is **too**.

6 **Spelling six**: the word is **imagine**.
They were asked to **imagine** their favourite place.
The word is **imagine**.

7 **Spelling seven**: the word is **tomorrow**.
The visitors would be coming to the school **tomorrow**.
The word is **tomorrow**.

8 **Spelling eight**: the word is **create**.
The task was to **create** a model of the solar system.
The word is **create**.

9 **Spelling nine**: the word is **investigate**.
The police had to **investigate** the crime.
The word is **investigate**.

10 **Spelling ten**: the word is **bookmark**.
The lady used a **bookmark** to show which page she had got to.
The word is **bookmark**.

PAGE 83 SPELLING TASK LEVEL 6

1 **Spelling one**: the word is **receipt**.
The items bought were listed on the **receipt**.
The word is **receipt**.

2 **Spelling two**: the word is **questionnaire**.
All the parents were sent a **questionnaire** to fill out.
The word is **questionnaire**.

3 **Spelling three**: the word is **broccoli**.
The boy ate everything except his **broccoli!**
The word is **broccoli**.

4 **Spelling four**: the word is **citizen**.
He was a **citizen** of the country.
The word is **citizen**.

5 **Spelling five**: the word is **seize**.
The police had to **seize** the thief quickly.
The word is **seize**.

6 **Spelling six**: the word is **doubt**.
There was **doubt** as to whether he was the author.
The word is **doubt**.

7 **Spelling seven**: the word is **business**.
The shop had enjoyed good **business** during the holiday.
The word is **business**.

8 **Spelling eight**: the word is **woollen**.
It was a bright red **woollen** jumper.
The word is **woollen**.

9 **Spelling nine**: the word is **dictionary**.
They looked the word up in the **dictionary**.
The word is **dictionary**.

10 **Spelling ten**: the word is **suspicious**.
The boy acted in a **suspicious** way.
The word is **suspicious**.

Words ending in 'l'

For one syllable words ending in 'l', simply add the suffix.

For words with two or more syllables ending in 'l', double the final 'l' and then add the suffix.

Add the suffix shown to each of these words to change the way they are used.

1 identical (-y) _____

2 school (-ing) _____

3 soul (-fully) _____

4 beautiful (-y) _____

5 ail (-ment) _____

6 pencil (-ed) _____

Words ending in 'e'

Usually when you add a suffix that starts with a vowel to a word ending in 'e', you drop the 'e' from the word.

Add the suffixes shown to the following words to change the way they are used. Put a cross in the box if it does not make a proper word. The first one has been done for you.

Root word	+ -ing	+ -ed
hope	hoping	hoped
love		
shame		
make		
shake		
assume		
take		

More complex prefixes and suffixes

What is a more complex prefix?

A more complex prefix is one that is not used as regularly as the more common ones, e.g inter- (interact). It is important that you use a range of vocabulary to demonstrate your higher levels of writing.

Circle the correct prefix to change the meaning of these words.

1 **regular**:   anti- / ag- / as- / ir-

2 **legal**:   anti- / il- / ag- / af-

3 **vantage**:   af- / a- / as- / ad-

4 **vent**:   ad- / il- / al- / as-

5 **custom**:   af- / ad- / ac- / il-

More prefixes

Write three words that begin with the following prefixes:

1   ab-

_____

_____

_____

2   anti-

_____

_____

_____

3   il-

_____

_____

_____

4   af-

_____

_____

_____

5   ap-

_____

_____

_____

Complex suffixes

A suffix can be added to a noun to create a verb.

Complete the table below to change these nouns to verbs. The first one has been done for you.

Noun	Suffix to add	Verb
book	-ed	booked
terror		
advert		
liquid		
critic		
	-ify	
	-ate	
	-ise	
	-en	

Top Tip

Remember a verb is a 'doing' word. So the suffixes you might add to change a noun to a verb are '-ise', '-ify', '-ate', or 'en' among others.

Complex prefix or suffix?

Circle the complex prefixes and suffixes in the following words.

1 legality
2 classify
3 intoxicate
4 adjourn
5 notify
6 illegality
7 illuminate
8 antifreeze

Top Tip

Some words will have a complex prefix and suffix.

Vowels and consonants

What are the vowels?

Write down the five vowels in the English language:

Consonants

Write a definition to explain what a consonant is.

_____

_____

Remember that sometimes the letter 'y' can act as a vowel sound in words.

Top Tip

Spot the vowel sound

Every word contains a vowel sound.

Circle the letters that create the vowel sound in the following words.

1 over

2 concern

3 through

4 fly

5 rely

6 cat

7 swim

8 umbrella

9 unify

10 cried

Spotting consonants

Circle the words that contain at least three **different** consonants.

endless	suspect	soon	trouble
tube	Sussex	needless	when
was	Mississippi		

Consonants making different sounds

A consonant can make different sounds in different words.

The consonant **h** can make two different sounds in words – one where the 'h' is heard and the other where it is silent. Fill in the table to show examples of this. You can use a dictionary to help you.

Making the sound 'h'	Not making the sound 'h'
hair	hour

The consonant **g** can make three different sounds in words – one where the 'g' is heard as a 'g'; one where it is heard as a 'j'; and one where it is heard as 'zh'. Fill in the table to show examples of this. You can use a dictionary to help you.

Making the sound 'g'	Making the sound 'j'	Making the sound 'zh'
gap	agent	beige

Homophones and homonyms

What are homophones?

Homophones are words that sound the same, but are spelt differently.

Underline the correct spelling of the word to make these sentences correct.

1 Mum decided to poor / pour the milk from the jug.

2 It was time for there / their coach to arrive.

3 I had a grate / great time at my friend's house.

4 Queen Victoria reigned / rained for a long time.

5 There are to / too many children on the bus.

6 They're / There very noisy today!

7 They had to put flower / flour in the cake mixture.

8 The children played a game of pairs / pears with the cards.

Alternative homophones

Write a homophone for each of these words.

1 stares _____

2 wear _____

3 air _____

4 tail _____

5 medal _____

6 forth _____

7 blue _____

8 beach _____

9 hair _____

10 reed _____

Top Tip

You need to check your sentences as using the wrong homophone could make them sound very silly! (e.g. The bare was chasing the buoy!)

What are homonyms?

Homonyms are words that have the same spelling but different meanings.

Write an alternative definition for each of these homonyms.

1 wave

Definition 1: when a long body of water breaks on the shoreline.

Definition 2: _____

2 bat

Definition 1: a nocturnal creature that hangs upside down.

Definition 2: _____

3 watch

Definition 1: to look or observe closely over a period of time.

Definition 2: _____

4 ring

Definition 1: the act of causing a bell to sound.

Definition 2: _____

Spot the homonyms and homophones

Underline the homonyms in the passages below and circle the homophone mistakes.

1 Kangaroos often live in Australia. There legs are long and extend to help them jump long distances. That is why they are good jumpers.

2 The children were going on a school trip. The coach was going to drive them to the museum wear they would have a grate time!

3 The tennis match was going to be between the two best players. They had worked hard to improve there game. They staired at each other from across the caught.

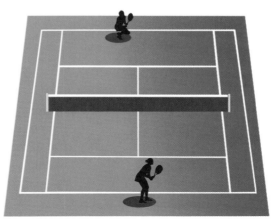

Spelling strategies 1

Look / Say / Cover / Write / Check

Use the 'look / say / cover / write and check' method to see how well you have learned your spellings. Look at your list of spellings that you have to learn, say them out loud, cover them over and then write them down. Then look back at your original spellings and check how well you have done. If you have made mistakes, look carefully at these words and have another go.

Choose five of the spellings from your own list and practise using this method:

1 _____   2 _____

3 _____   4 _____

5 _____

Words within words

You can often spot short words (that you can already spell) within longer words. This can help you with spelling the harder words.

Highlight or underline the short words that are hidden within these words.

| 1 create | 2 encounter | 3 definite |
| 4 smartly | 5 sphere | 6 hearty |

Air writing

Pretend your finger is a large whiteboard marker. Write the words in the air as if you are writing on a big whiteboard.

Try air writing these words.

| 1 protect | 2 revise | 3 yacht |
| 4 talent | 5 telescope | 6 horizon |

Top Tip

By doing this, your brain is remembering the patterns of the word. This can help you to think about the spelling when writing the word on paper.

Write it in an exciting way

You can use colouring pens and highlighters to write the words in different ways so that your brain can remember them. Try picking out the unusual or tricky parts of the words and write them in a different colour to the rest of the word.

Write the following words in the space below using coloured pens / highlighters to pick out the tricky or unusual parts.

1	privilege	**2**	moisture	**3**	convince
4	lenient	**5**	familiar	**6**	height

Syllable hunting

Breaking a word into syllables can help you remember each part of the spelling.

Break the following words into syllables and then say each word aloud in syllables.

Example: tomorrow = to-mor-row

1 vocabulary = _____

2 satisfy = _____

3 exaggerate = _____

4 explanation = _____

5 similar = _____

Top Tip

Every syllable usually has a vowel. 'Y' can act as a vowel sound in words.

Spelling strategies 2

Saying it as it is spelt

Another way of breaking up the words is to say them as they are spelt. This can help you remember when there are hidden letters.

Try saying the words below, which have been broken up into how they are spelt.

1 Feb-ru-ary

2 Wed-nes-day

3 happ-i-ness

4 bus-i-ness

5 jewel-le-ry

6 mi-ra-cle

Mnemonics

Mnemonics are a fun way to learn spelling. You assign a word to each letter of the word you need to spell to make a rhyme.

For example: BECAUSE = Brave Elephants Can Always Use Special Eggs

The sillier the rhyme the better, as it may help you to remember the spelling!

Write mnemonics for these tricky words:

1 debate

_____

2 bruise

_____

3 knead

_____

4 sign

_____

5 yacht

_____

6 equip

_____

Rapping

Some words can be learned using a chant or rap.

Say each letter in a rhythmic way and make up fun raps and chants,
e.g. W – A – R – D – R – O – B – E spells...WARDROBE

Try making up a chant for these words.

1 harass **2** favour **3** garage

4 century **5** surprise **6** union

Drawing Pictures

Sometimes it can help to draw a picture of the word you are learning. For example, if the word is wheel you can write the word in the shape of a wheel. This can help make it easier to remember as you can remember seeing the word on the page in that pattern and seeing the shape of the letters.

Try 'drawing' pictures with these words.

1 mountain **2** valley **3** wave

4 saucepan **5** sandwich **6** cloud

Black list

Make a list of spellings that you often spell wrong (the 'black list'!). Keep adding to this list as you come across new words you struggle with. Use the strategies above to try and learn them in different ways so that they come off the 'black list'.

Top Tip

If one strategy for spelling the word doesn't work, try a different one. It is a good idea to use a range of strategies as this keeps you interested in learning!

53

Word families, roots and origins

Identify the root words

In English, many words are derived from other words, which are called root words. Root words may appear anywhere in a word, e.g. **act**ivity, re**act**, inter**act**ion.

Underline the roots in these words.

1 aquarium

2 biology

3 democracy

4 geography

5 reject

6 sympathy

7 transport

8 zoology

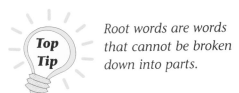

Top Tip

Root words are words that cannot be broken down into parts.

Word families using roots

Write three words that contain the following root words. You can use a dictionary to help you.

1 port

_____

_____

_____

3 geo

_____

_____

_____

2 neuro

_____

_____

_____

4 equ

_____

_____

_____

Match the origin

With a line, match each root word to its meaning

ROOT WORD	MEANING
aqua	form
demo	animal
loc	small
min	people
morph	water
zoo	place

Top Tip

*To work out the meaning of the root word, think about words that contain the root and what they mean, e.g. democracy is about the **people**.*

Word families and meanings

For each root word below, look at the definition and then find three words that are part of that word family. Use a dictionary to help you. One example has been given for you.

1 **multi** (meaning many):

multiply _____ _____

2 **arch** (meaning chief / leader / ruler):

_____ _____ _____

3 **chrom** (meaning colour):

_____ _____ _____

4 **cred** (meaning believe):

_____ _____ _____

5 **equ** (meaning equal):

_____ _____ _____

6 **pater** (meaning father):

_____ _____ _____

7 **voc** (meaning call):

_____ _____ _____

8 **spec** (meaning look / see):

_____ _____ _____

More complex word families

Form-based families

Form-based families are word families where there are common root words or letter strings between them.

Write words that have the following common letter strings or root words and are similar in form.

Example: family – familiar – unfamiliar – familiarity – familiarise

1 word   – _____

2 teach   – _____

3 final   – _____

4 improve – _____

5 behave   – _____

6 book   – _____

Word-webs

Create a word-web containing at least 10 words containing the common letter string 'ology'. Two examples have been given for you.

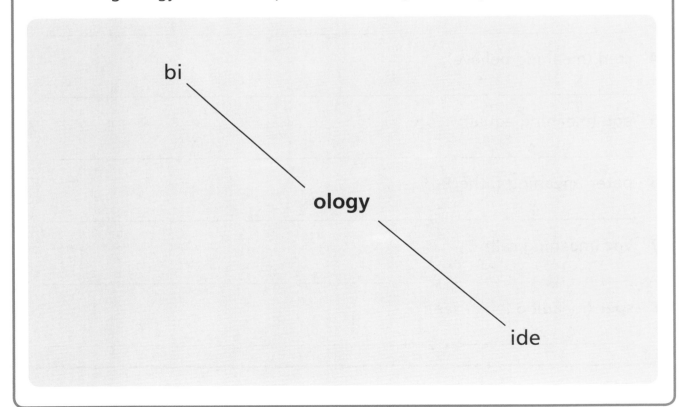

Meaning-based families

Some words are related in meaning but not in form.

For example: book = page, literacy, literature, bookshop, read, write, author, etc...

Write eight meaning-based word family words for each of the following:

1 school = _____

_____

2 mammal = _____

_____

3 food = _____

_____

4 hospital = _____

_____

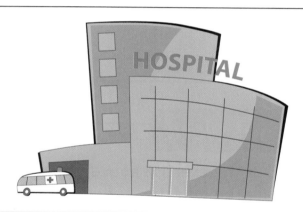

Word-webs

Create a meaning-based word-web for the word 'pen'.

pen

Inflectional endings

What is an inflectional ending?

An inflectional ending is an inflection that is added at the end of a root word, very much like a suffix!

Add the inflectional endings to the words in the table. The first one has been done for you.

Root word	+ er	+ ing	+ ed
travel	traveller	travelling	travelled
walk			
amble			
clap			
milk			

Changes to the root word

As you may have noticed in the exercise above, the root word sometimes has to change to accommodate the inflectional ending.

Write the rules that apply to the following words before the inflectional ending is added.

Example: travel + er = traveller

Rule: double the final consonant of travel and add the inflectional ending.

1   create + ion = _____

    Rule: _____

    _____

2   wrestle + ing = _____

    Rule: _____

    _____

Changes to the root word

3 easy + est = _____

Rule: _____

_____

4 collective + ism = _____

Rule: _____

_____

5 trap + ing = _____

Rule: _____

_____

6 hop + ed = _____

Rule: _____

_____

Further examples

Using the rules for changing the root word that you found in the previous exercise, write two more examples for each type of root word and inflectional ending.

One example has been done for you.

1 Using root like 'create' + 'ion':

rotate + ion = rotation _____

2 Using root like 'wrestle' + 'ing':

_____ _____

3 Using root like 'easy' + 'est':

_____ _____

4 Using root like 'collective' + 'ism':

_____ _____

5 Using root like 'trap' + 'ing':

_____ _____

6 Using root like 'hop' + 'ed':

_____ _____

Editing skills

Spelling and punctuation errors

When reading through your work, make sure that you check your sentences have been correctly punctuated and that spellings are correct.

Edit the piece of text below by correcting the misspelt words and adding in the missing or incorrect punctuation.

> it was a cold windy and wet day in the middle of febuary. The ground was wet from the rain that had fallen nonstop for sevral days. james was sitting in his room feeling fed up he just wanted to be able to go out and play on his new bike

Repetition of words

In the paragraph, underline the repeated words and rewrite the paragraph so that it is more interesting for the reader.

> I was so excited about the weekend because I was going to be the carnival princess. I was chosen because I won the competition in the local paper. I was going to wear a beautiful gold dress with a beautiful tiara and beautiful silver shoes. I was going to look beautiful. My excitement disappeared when I looked at the weather.

_____

_____

_____

_____

_____

_____

_____

_____

Top Tip

When reading through your work, check that it is not boring for your reader. If you repeat the same words at the start of sentences it becomes very dull to read.

Sentences making sense

When writing, you can often get so involved in what you are writing that you miss words out of sentences by accident. This means that the sentences, when read back, do not make sense. It is important to read back through your work to check for these sorts of errors.

Correct the errors in the passage below and add in any missing words.

> The door creaked open and all I could sea was darkness. Before my eyes could become accustomed to the dark there was loud bang. I looked left and write. What was I to do? The door had swung shut me. I was trapped. The sounds began again; I put my hands my ears. I curled up small and hoped that someone, anyone, would come rescue me.

Editing a piece of writing

It is important to use a range of connectives, as well as varied sentences and vocabulary to keep your writing interesting for your reader.

Rewrite the passage so that it is more interesting for your reader, using varied connectives, vocabulary, checking your spelling and punctuation and adding extra exciting details.

> I went on holiday to Spain and had a very good time. The weather was warm and I stayed in a nice hotel. One day it did rain but I still had fun. I stayed in the hotel and went in the indoor pool. The activities I did were fun and I met lots of new people. I liked paragliding best because I liked being high up. I didn't like going on the jet-ski because it went too fast. I enjoyed the food because I tried lots of different things. I would like to go back to Spain because I had such fun.

_____

_____

_____

_____

_____

_____

_____

_____

Antonyms and synonyms

What are synonyms?

A synonym is a word or phrase that means exactly or nearly the same as another word or phrase.

Write three synonyms for each of the words given below.

1 said _____

2 happy _____

3 fun _____

4 nice _____

5 very _____

Top Tip

Synonyms can enhance your writing as they prevent you using the same word too many times and boring your reader!

Enhancing writing with synonyms

Rewrite this passage using synonyms for the repeated words.

> I went to the park. I went on the swings and had fun. I went on the slide and had fun. It was nice when I went on the roundabout because it was fun. I had fun at the park as it was a nice sunny day. I would like to have more fun at the park when the weather is nice again.

_____

_____

_____

_____

_____

_____

_____

Antonyms

Antonyms are words that are opposite in meaning to another word.

Write an antonym for each of these words.

1   happy   _____

2   dry   _____

3   warm   _____

4   heavy   _____

5   deep   _____

6   early   _____

7   stop   _____

8   tall   _____

9   old   _____

10 pretty _____

Using antonyms in writing

Change the underlined words to suitable antonyms and rewrite the sentences.

1   The <u>hot</u> toast tasted good!

_____

2   The <u>ugly</u> frog kissed the <u>beautiful</u> princess.

_____

3   The <u>slow</u> fish darted along the <u>slow</u> moving river.

_____

4   The <u>happy</u> child played with the <u>soft</u> teddy.

_____

5   The <u>new</u> teacher was excited to meet her <u>naughty</u> class.

_____

Speech vocabulary

Which type of speech?

There are two types of speech: reported and direct.

Write (D) next to the examples of direct speech and (R) next to the examples of reported speech.

1 'I am learning lots of interesting things about grammar," said George. _____

2 Trevor whispered to his mum, 'Can we go home now?" _____

3 Sam said that he wanted a toy car for his birthday. _____

4 "I wish I had a BMX bike," moaned Jacob. _____

5 George said that he liked learning about grammar. _____

Using correct speech punctuation

Rewrite this reported speech as a direct speech conversation using the correct layout features and punctuation (add extra details if you wish).

The teacher explained that the class would be going on a visit to a science museum at the end of the month. Daniel was not impressed and said that he would rather go to a dark cave. Ryan asked where the museum was. Miss Dawson, the teacher, said it was in London. Sarah burst in to tears and said that she would get travel sick on the coach. Freya said that she had been there before and it was brilliant and she couldn't wait to go again. Joe said that he wanted to find out more about how the Earth was formed. Daniel said again that he wished he could go anyway else but there. Miss Dawson asked the children to be quiet so that she could tell them more about it. She told them that they would be split into small groups to be able to see the exhibits better. Daniel grunted that he would probably end up in her group because he always had to go with the teacher. Miss Dawson frowned at him. Ryan whispered to Sam that he hoped he was in his group. Freya whispered to Georgia that she wanted to be with her. Joe shouted across the room to Jacob that they could be in a group together. Miss Dawson raised her head above the din and shouted for the children to stop talking. She ended by saying that she thought it would be easier to just cancel the visit altogether!

Using correct speech punctuation

Singular and plural

What does singular and plural mean?

Something in its singular form is when you are writing or talking about **one** thing on its own. Plural means when there is **more than one** of something.

Write whether these are plural or singular items.

1 cats _____

2 boat _____

3 babies _____

4 friend _____

5 men _____

6 children _____

Words ending in 's' when they are singular

Remember to add 'es' if a word in its singular form ends in an 's'.

Change these words to their plural form:

1 bus _____

2 fortress _____

3 kiss _____

4 witness _____

5 gas _____

Top Tip

It is important to remember this, otherwise you could end up with words with three 's' in a row, e.g, 'dresss', which would be wrong.

Singular words ending in 'y'

When a word in its singular form ends in a 'y', the 'y' is **usually** replaced with 'ies'.

Write the plurals of these examples.

1 pony _____

2 day _____

3 canary _____

4 spy _____

5 puppy _____

6 fairy _____

Top Tip

There are exceptions to this rule where you just add an 's' after the 'y'. You need to learn the common exceptions, e.g. toys, boys, plays, rays.

Singular words ending in 'f'

When a word in its singular form ends in a 'f', the 'f' is **usually** replaced with 'ves'.

Turn these singular words into plurals.

1 loaf _____

2 shelf _____

3 wolf _____

4 half _____

Top Tip *There are exceptions to this rule where you just add an 's' at the end of the word, e.g. roofs.*

Singular words ending in 'o'

When a word in its singular form ends with a 'o', the letters 'es' are **usually** added after the 'o' to make it plural.

Write these words in their plural form.

1 video _____

2 echo _____

3 volcano _____

4 hero _____

5 mango _____

6 domino _____

Top Tip *There are exceptions to this rule where you just add an 's' after the 'o'. You need to learn the common exceptions, e.g. kilos, pianos.*

Technical vocabulary

What is technical vocabulary?

Choose words from the list to fill in the gaps and complete the sentences about technical vocabulary.

contents	glossary	index	subject-specific
fiction	non-fiction	spelling	definition
easy	technical		

Technical vocabulary is _____ vocabulary. It is often found in _____ books where difficult concepts are explained. These books contain a _____ where the _____ of the _____ words is given.

Where would you find technical vocabulary?

Circle the texts that you would expect to find technical vocabulary in.

a letter to a friend   a newspaper

poetry   books for babies

fairytales   non-chronological reports

report texts   a postcard

recipes

Spot the technical vocabulary

Circle the technical vocabulary in the passage below.

Microscopes have played a large part in the understanding of medicine. They allow researchers to examine microscopic items in a huge amount of detail. The magnification can be changed and adapted based on the specimen being examined. Scientists have made huge breakthroughs and will continue to do so with the help of some equipment.

Top Tip

When identifying technical vocabulary, take time to understand the subject that is being explained, as this will help you identify the words that are specific to this text.

Using technical vocabulary in sentences

Complete these sentences, using technical vocabulary.

1   The Big Bang theory is used by _____ to explain the

beginning of the world.

2   The _____ is used by _____ to study the

night sky.

3   The process of _____ is when water is heated by the sun.

4   _____ flows from a volcano when it

_____, covering everything and anyone in its path.

Using technical vocabulary

Choose a science topic that you know lots about (e.g. the water cycle, magnetism, friction) and write a short, yet detailed report about it for a child your age, using technical vocabulary. When you have finished, underline the technical vocabulary that you have used.

_____

_____

_____

_____

_____

_____

_____

_____

_____

_____

Figurative language

Personification

Personification is when a non-human thing is described using human characteristics.

Match the correct word to the personification description.

1 The snowman   ...glared down from the sky.

2 Summer   ...ran wild among the trees.

3 The storm   ...is a woman with long golden hair.

4 Fire   ...danced in the moonlight

5 The sun   ...swallowed the houses.

6 The ocean   ...is a chubby boy wrapped up warm.

Alliteration

Alliteration is when the same letter or sound is used at the beginning of adjacent or closely connected words.

Finish these sentences using alliteration.

1 Wind whistles _____

2 Big, black _____

3 Seven seals _____

4 Ten tractors _____

5 Fish flip _____

Top Tip

Identify the repeated letter or sound first. Use this in your writing to emphasise descriptions but be careful not to overuse it!

Assonance

Assonance is different from alliteration; it is the repetition of vowel sounds within words to create internal rhyming, e.g. *Murmuring of innumerable bees*.

Write (A) next to the sentences that use assonance and (L) next to the ones that use alliteration.

1 I try to light the fire.   A

2 Mickey Mouse makes mince pies.   L

Assonance

3 He went round the mound listening for the sound.   `Á`

4 The fox locks his socks in a box.   `A`

5 I buy a fly swat.   ☐

6 The bed sheet billowed, boldly in the breeze.   `L`

Onomatopoeia

Onomatopoeia is when a word is formed from a sound associated with it, e.g. CRACK.

In the box below, write 10 onomatopoeia words, like those that you might find in a comic strip.

Which is which?

Use the following letters to identify each sentence: P for personification, A for assonance, L for alliteration and O for onomatopoeia.

1 The tree danced in the breeze.   ☐

2 Pretty Polly poured pear juice into the glass.   ☐

3 The mouse squeaked.   ☐

4 The white knight fights.   ☐

5 The water chattered merrily in the brook.   ☐

6 The branch creaked eerily.   ☐

Personal form and impersonal form

What is the impersonal language form?

Put a tick next to the correct characteristics of impersonal language and put a cross next to the incorrect characteristics.

1   Use of personal pronouns, e.g. I

2   Use of impersonal subject

3   Use of judgemental words to indicate your feelings

4   Use of emotive words

5   Use of evidence to back up view

6   Use of the passive voice

When is it used?

Circle the types of texts where formal, impersonal language must be used.

legal document   poetry

information text   play script

e-mail to a friend   balanced argument

Top Tip

Identify the audience and purpose of the text to ascertain which type of language, and the formality, that is to be used.

Formal or informal?

Write the letter (F) if you should use formal language and (I) if you should use informal language when communicating in the following scenarios.

1   A meeting with a work colleague.

2   An e-mail to the headteacher.

3   A national newspaper report.

4   An e-mail to a friend.

5   A debate.

6   A guidebook for a museum.

7   A shopping list.

8   A non-chronological report.

Writing formally and impersonally

Write your views about an issue that is important to you, e.g. school uniform, saving the planet, recycling. Write in a formal and impersonal style.

_____

_____

_____

_____

_____

_____

_____

_____

_____

_____

Writing informally

Look at the text you have written in the box above. Now rewrite the same paragraph but in an informal, personal form.

_____

_____

_____

_____

_____

_____

_____

_____

_____

_____

_____

Short answer questions

The questions on pages 74–79 provide test practice for the type of questions you will find on **Paper 1: short answer questions** (Levels 3–5).

1 Tick one box to show where the missing **exclamation mark** should go.

The teacher shouted "Stop" before the child ran across the road.

☐ ☐ ☐   ☐ **1 mark**

2 Complete the sentences below using either **is**, **were** or **was**.

The children _____ playing in the park.

Today, Simon _____ still Tom's best friend.

The baby _____ crying very loudly!   **1 mark**

3 imogen went to london in may to see her friend.

a) Circle the three words in the sentence above that should start with a capital letter.

b) For one of these words, explain why it needs a capital letter.
   Word chosen _____

   _____   **2 marks**

4 The boys <u>watched</u> the <u>elephant</u> from a distance. <u>They</u> <u>stayed</u> quiet so as not to scare it.

Put a tick in each row to show whether each underlined word is a verb, noun or pronoun.

Word from the sentence	Noun	Verb	Pronoun
watched			
elephant			
They			
stayed			

1 mark

5 You are looking over your work and decide to replace the word 'nice' in the sentence below.

The food was nice.

Choose a synonym and write it in the box. [   ]   **1 mark**

Short answer questions

1 Circle the **prepositions** in this sentence.

The thief ran across the road and the car swerved into the tree. **1 mark**

2 Tick **one** word to complete the sentence below so that it is grammatically correct.

The girl said that she should _____ told the truth.

off ☐

of ☐

have ☐

had ☐ **1 mark**

3 Write a **connective** from the boxes in each space to complete the sentences below. Use each word once.

and	however	otherwise

Today it was raining _____ it had been sunny the day before. Jason

_____ Ross were glad that they had tested their rocket yesterday

_____ they would not have been able to see it work at all. **1 mark**

4 Which sentences describe the use of **paragraphs**? Tick **two**

Paragraphs can signal a change of action ☐

Paragraphs always signal a change of action ☐

Paragraphs always include a proper noun ☐

Paragraphs help to organise longer texts ☐ **1 mark**

5 Which of the sentences below is punctuated correctly? Tick **one**

Its been a lovely day and the dog enjoyed it's walk ☐

It's been a lovely day and the dog enjoyed its walk ☐

It's been a lovely day and the dog enjoyed it's walk ☐

Its been a lovely day and the dog enjoyed its walk ☐ **1 mark**

Short answer questions

6 Insert **two** commas in the correct place in the sentence below.

The children who were all in the same class visited the swimming pool.

1 mark

7 Write one letter in each box to show the **word class**.

adjective	noun	adverb	verb
A	B	C	D

The noisy elephant happily squirted water at the angry keeper.

☐ ☐ ☐   ☐

1 mark

8 Put a tick in each row to show whether the **main** or **subordinate** clause is in bold.

An example is shown.

	Main clause	Subordinate clause
The boys, who were all nine, **swam across the pool**.	✔	
The roof collapsed because of the weight of snow.		
The lady ran quickly, **because she was late**.		
The teacher, who was called Claire, **worked extremely hard all day**.		

2 marks

9 Change this sentence from reported speech to direct speech.

Eliza said that she was going to work much harder at grammar from now on.

_____ **1 mark**

10 Find **one** word that can complete **both** sentences below.

Write the word in the box.

The box was _____ so she was able to carry it.

It was time to switch off the _____ so he could go to sleep.

☐

1 mark

Short answer questions

1 Put an **article** in each sentence below to ensure it makes sense.

_____ children walked to school.

It was sunset and time for _____ school to be locked up.

Jasmine looked up and _____ apple fell from _____ tree above her.

1 mark

2 Which two of these sentences are **complex**?   Tick **two**

The prize, a glittering gold cup, stood on the table at the front. ☐

The prize was a glittering gold cup ☐

The nosiest girl, whose name was Karen, did not win the prize. ☐

The boys from the smartest team won the prize. ☐

The prize was stolen ☐

1 mark

3 Which of these is the correct pluralisation of the word **pony**?

Tick **one**

ponys ☐

ponies ☐

ponyes ☐

pony's ☐   **1 mark**

4 Circle the **subordinating connective** in the sentence below.

After the earthquake, the buildings were destroyed.   **1 mark**

5 Look at the passage below. Change all the verbs from the **future** tense to the **past** tense.

The birds <u>will be flying</u> over the house.

⬆

[_____]

I <u>will be</u> good at my grammar test.

⬆

[_____]   **2 marks**

Short answer questions

6 Which of the sentences below is punctuated correctly?   Tick **one**

The (girl from across the road) who is also my friend was not very well. ☐

The girl from across the road (who is also my friend) was not very well. ☐

The girl from across the road who is (also my friend) was not very well. ☐

The girl from across the road who is also my friend (was not very well). ☐

1 mark

7 Draw lines to match the words with another word that can be joined to it using a hyphen.

water		wheel
red		three
twenty		hot

1 mark

8 Look at this sentence:

The animals lined up (eight dogs and six cats) ready to start the race.

a) What is the name of the punctuation mark that is used twice in this sentence? _____

b) Why is this punctuation mark used in the sentence above?   Tick **one**

To mark the start of a new sentence ☐

To signal that someone is speaking ☐

To separate a group of words in a sentence ☐

To mark an expectant pause ☐   **1 mark**

9 Draw lines to match the punctuation marks shown in the sentences with their names.

Use each punctuation mark **once**.

Sentence	Name of punctuation
I had to pack: six shirts	colon
The door creaked open slowly…	hyphen
The ninety-nine bottles sat on the wall	ellipsis

1 mark

Short answer questions

The questions on this page are designed to give practice for the spelling questions in the short answer paper.

1 The sentences below each have an error. The errors are underlined. Write the correction in the box, choosing the correct homophone.

The tree had lots of <u>pairs</u> on it.

I had a <u>grate</u> time on holiday.

2 marks

2 A prefix is a letter or group of letters added to the beginning of a word to make a new word, e.g. <u>un</u>usual.

Put a prefix at the beginning of each word to make it mean the opposite.

_____virus

_____nutrition

_____happy

1 mark

3 Tick one word to complete the sentence below.

The children sat and ate _____ lunches quietly.

there ☐

their ☐

they're ☐

1 mark

4 Write three words using the root word 'port'.

_____ _____ _____

1 mark

5 Circle the correct spelling below.

hurryed / hurried / hurrieyed

1 mark

Spelling

The questions on this page are designed to provide test practice for **Paper 2: spelling** (Levels 3–5).

It is just the answer lines that are given below. You will need to ask someone to read the instructions and sentences to you. These can be found on p12 of the answer booklet.

1 The boy _____ about the answer.

2 She was _____ with her test result.

3 The children were _____ in the playground.

4 The train would _____ at the station.

5 It was _____ long for the children to wait.

6 They were asked to _____ their favourite place.

7 The visitors would be coming to the school _____.

8 The task was to _____ a model of the solar system.

9 The police has to _____ the crime.

10 The lady used a _____ to show which page she had got to.

Short answer questions

The questions on pages 81–82 provide test practice for the type of questions you will find on **Paper 2: short answer questions** (Level 6).

1 The sentence below is written in the **passive** voice.

The window was broken by the boy.

Which sentence is the **active** form of the sentence above?   Tick **one**

The window, which was delicate, was broken. ☐

The boy broke the window. ☐

Because the boy was naughty, he broke the window. ☐

The boy and the window were broken. ☐   **1 mark**

2 Expand the noun into a noun phrase by adding words before **and** after the noun. One has been done for you.

Noun	Noun phrase
the computer	the expensive computer on the desk
the car	

1 mark

3 Rewrite the sentence below, changing the verbs to **present** tense.

The team played well in their football match and won the game.

_____   **1 mark**

4 Put a tick in each row to show the type of noun shown.

Noun	Abstract	Collective	Common	Proper
a flock				
Cambridge				
glass				
hope				

1 mark

5 Circle the correct form of the verb in each set of brackets.

The team (train / trains) at the local park.

Each child (is / are) allowed one parent to attend.

Children (have / has) to be the future of our country.   **1 mark**

Short answer questions

The questions on this page are designed to give test practice for the spelling questions in the short answer paper.

1 Put a tick in each row to show which prefix would be used to make it mean the opposite.

	un-	dis-	de-
respect			
helpful			
classify			

1 mark

2 Add a suffix to this word to make a **verb**.

terror_____   **1 mark**

3 Underline the root word in each of these words:

prescription

transportation

multiplication   **1 mark**

4 Write three words with the common letter string 'ough'.

_____   _____   _____   **1 mark**

5 Circle the correct English spelling below.

jewellary / jewellry / jewellery / jewelary   **1 mark**

The questions on this page are designed to give test practice for **Paper 3: spelling** (Level 6).

It is just the answer lines that are given below. You will need to ask someone to read the instructions and sentences to you. These can be found on p12 of the answer booklet.

1 The items bought were listed on the _____.

2 All the parents were sent a _____ to fill out.

3 The boy ate everything except his _____!

4 He was a _____ of the country.

5 The police had to _____ the thief quickly.

6 There was _____ as to whether he was the author.

7 The shop had enjoyed good _____ during the holiday.

8 It was a bright red _____ jumper.

9 They looked the word up in the _____.

10 The boy acted in a _____ way.

Extended task

The question on this page is designed to give test practice for
Paper 1: extended task (Level 6)

In the extended writing task (Level 6 paper only), your **grammar, punctuation** and **vocabulary** will be tested in a piece of writing. The focus for the task should be on the range of sentence structures and punctuation marks you use to control your writing.

Spelling will not be assessed in this task. Try to use a wide range of ambitious vocabulary in your response.

You will have 30 minutes for this task.

Advertise My School

The Governors at your school are trying to encourage more parents to send their children to your school. The headteacher thinks that a leaflet campaign for the local area would help to boost numbers.

They have decided that the leaflet would be best if it was produced by the children currently at the school (you!). The content will need to include some of the following topics:

- How the classes are organised
- Clubs that children can attend
- School uniform
- The playground
- How ICT helps with learning
- Lessons that are taught

You can add ideas of your own that you think would help to make your school sound appealing.

Your task is to write the wording for the leaflet.

Acknowledgements

Cover and P1 © Mayboroda /Shutterstock, © Petr Vaclavek/ Shutterstock; P04 © Ken Benner/Shutterstock.com; P05 © NeilRas/Shutterstock.com; P07 © Matthew Cole/Shutterstock. com; P09 © NeilRas/Shutterstock.com; P11 © blinkblink/ Shutterstock; P16 © Kemo/Shutterstock.com; P17 © Morphart Creation/Shutterstock.com; P22 © benchart/Shutterstock. com; P24 © Matthew Cole/Shutterstock.com; P28 © Morphart Creation/Shutterstock.com; P31 © iadams/Shutterstock.com;

P37 © Roman Sotola/Shutterstock.com; P39 © Morphart Creation/Shutterstock.com; P43 © Mahesh Patil/Shutterstock. com; P46 © Irina Matskevich/Shutterstock.com; P48 © U.P.images_vector/Shutterstock.com; P49 © charobnica/Shutterstock. com; P57 © Svinkin/Shutterstock.com; P63 © Yobidaba/ Shutterstock.com; P67 © J Miks/Shutterstock, ©OK-SANA/ Shutterstock; P69 © Morphart Creation/Shutterstock.com